Cross Currents

IN THE WAKE OF THE GREAT WAR

Marita E. Ritsche

from
Marita E. Ritsche

D1554383

Cover Photo: Theodor and Adolf Ritsche after their arrival in Minnesota

Cross Currents

IN THE WAKE OF THE GREAT WAR

Marita E. Ritsche

Milwaukee, Wisconsin

Copyright © 2005 by Marita E. Ritsche

All rights reserved

Edited by Carolyn Kott Washburne

Cover and text design by Georgene Schreiner

No part of this publication may be reproduced, stored, or transmitted in any form or by any means, except for brief quotations not to exceed 100 words in a review of professional work, without the written permission of the author.

2009 08 07 06 05   5 4 3 2 1

Printed in the United States of America

First Edition - 2005

ISBN: 0-9749211-0-6

Library of Congress Control Number: 2004105481

Ritsche, Marita E.
    Cross currents : in the wake of the great war / Marita E. Ritsche. –
1st ed.– Milwaukee, WI : Transfluency Press, 2005.
    p. ; cm.
    English text, with German narrative.
    Includes bibliographical references.
    ISBN: 0-9749211-0-6
1. Ritsche, Marita E. 2. Germans United States–Biography. 3. German Americans–Social conditions. 4. Germany—Emigration and immigration–History–20th century. 5. United States–Emigration and immigration–History–20th century. 6. Germany–Economic conditions–1918-1945. 7. Germany–Social conditions–1918-1933. 8. World War, 1914-1918–Economic aspects–Germany. 9. Germany–History–1918-1933. I. Title.

E184.G3 .R58 2004   2004105481
973/.0431–dc22   0408

Project Coordination by Printstar Publishing, LLC
www.ppub.com

1527 W. County Line Rd. Milwaukee, WI 53217
www.transfluency.com

To the memory of my husband, Robert C. Eidt, who renewed my interest in my ethnic heritage.

To Gerhard Rauscher, in whose classes I gained my first insights into German cultural history from a native viewpoint.

Acknowledgments

Jerry Apps, Professor Emeritus, University of Wisconsin-Madison, who started me on the way to creative life-story writing;

Writers' Group (Maryelln Ebarp, Sara Filemyr, Jeane Knapp, Peg Mudroch, Barb Stampfl, Kathie Vogel, and Jeane Zarne), who encouraged me to exceed my original goals;

Sy Kreilein, PhD in German, and Don Zamzow, Charter President, Pommerscher Verein, Central Wisconsin, for professional advice on German language and culture;

The Printstar Publishing team, Nick, Carolyn, and Georgene, who maneuvered me through the publishing phase;

Emilie Ritsche Trushenski, who collected and preserved my parents' correspondence and photo albums and took the time to read the manuscript and make suggestions as did also long time friend, Jeff Kurth;

Tom Ritsche, who took the whole family to Germany in 1987, a gathering which rebound family ties not only on the east side of the Atlantic, but also in America;

Sherry Ritsche, who investigated and provided our father's documents for Ellis Island;

Siblings Em, Tom, Rich, Sherry, Estalee and Lanette, who sat with me from time to time around table or campfire, where we enjoyed each others' company and generated childhood memories;

Gerhard Rauscher, Professor Emeritus of German, University of Wisconsin-Milwaukee, and Richard Ritsche for their generous gifts of depression era Marks, some of which are reproduced herein.

CONTENTS

CROSS CURRENTS:
IN THE WAKE OF THE GREAT WAR

It is more than eighty years since the settlement of the Great War (1914-1918), now known as World War I, a good time to revisit its aftereffects. With hindsight, it is said, comes clearer "vision," more ability to put events into perspective.

Cross Currents: In the Wake of the Great War reminds us generally what most of our ancestors went through to provide us today in America with our comfortable standard of living. Specifically, it is intended to show how typical German-Americans felt and what they endured during a difficult century for those with German heritage.

It is, however, first and foremost the story of my father who, in 1923, along with his brother, made the decision to leave his beloved homeland in southwest Germany to seek better fortune in America. It is the story of the preparation for the trip starting in Meersburg, Germany, the crossing of the Atlantic, and, finally, the arrival at the home of their sponsors in Minnesota.

It is, furthermore, the story of a puzzling turn of events in the early twentieth century, which in some ways was justified, but in other ways not. For some time it had been hard for me to reconcile my view of my father with American stereotypes of Germans. Contrary to the usual stern adjectives applied to Germans, my father was overall a sentimental person, gentle and flexible in nature, a good family man, and, above all, deeply grateful for all that his adopted country had afforded him.

This work started out as a modest story about my family, primarily at this time about my dad. As I began to research the story's historical context, I reviewed the notes from my Master's degree in German over twenty-five years before. Imagine my surprise at discerning a broader interpretation of the world. The generally accepted facts were not wrong, they were simply incomplete. This second perusal a quarter century later prompted me to ask myself: What are the implications behind the broader historical facts?

Nevertheless, *Cross Currents: In the Wake of the Great War* is designed to appeal to various reader interests by putting the cultural data notes at the end of the work, thereby keeping the story essentially intact. Of course, some cultural references are needed in the text to reveal the reactions of the characters to the events around them.

Readers are encouraged to glean additional information through the notes. Those interested only in a story about immigration can omit glancing at them, but if you are ready to see the data with new eyes this period has much to reveal.

This book thus presents some of the lesser known historical facts surrounding the Great War in Europe and prior to the formation of the Third Reich. The presentation of the more obscure knowledge is intended to shed light on yet another example that this is an interdependent world, that there is no single agent of change but, rather, that every outcome depends on the interaction of all the historical ingredients. Germany's actions did not take place in a vacuum, but were, at least at first, reactions to others' moves. The reactive mode does not excuse the eventual atrocities, but a broader look at immediate post-Great War history does help us to understand how they came to pass.

I am suggesting that rather than accept the popular assumption that Germans alone are at fault for the tragedies in the aftermath of the Great War, for which they themselves took full responsibility when they signed the Versailles Treaty, there were also external influences that led Germany into its ignominious descent. At the same time, I caution construing the work as a mere legalistic ledger, that is, keeping score of the other party's injuries to one's own party. The numbers game has already done enough damage. Certain statistics are common knowledge, but when other statistics, equally important, are overlooked, the perspective is skewed. I maintain that these facts are not brought out for re-inspection with the intention of pointing fingers at other involved parties. However, until one's own culpability is acknowledged, the parties cannot move forward.

This process can be compared to family therapy. When a family member is brought in for counseling, modern family therapists will most likely say that this member is not the only one at fault. Rather, this person embodies and reflects most sharply the dysfunctional interaction of the entire family. Therefore, all family members should become involved if they want the family to heal. When a family meets, the wise therapist is careful to prevent sessions from turning into a free-for-all during which members dwell on their mutual injuries, for such will not lead to a solution.

Despite having presented the scene above, I see many positive events recently happening in central Europe that reveal a resolve toward an improved, more cooperative political future. On November 9, 1989, the Fall of the Berlin Wall, a non-violent event through the crumbling of the occupied power from within, reunited the two Germanies. In 1999 social critic Günther Grass received the Nobel Prize for Literature.[a] On January 22, 2003, France and Germany celebrated the Fortieth Anniversary of the Elysée Vertrag,[b] which supports mutual French and German teams and companies. In March 2003 Caroline Link won the Oscar in Hollywood for best foreign language film, "Nowhere in Africa,"[c] the story of a Jewish family that fled Nazi Germany for the wilds of Africa. On June 17, 2003, Germany celebrated the fiftieth anniversary of the uprising in former East Germany for the right, among others, to have free elections.[d] The news media, Deutsche Welle, dedicated from its beginning to demonstrate German democracy, celebrated its fiftieth anniversary.[e] German citizens, as advertised on the Deutsche Welle TV channel, are contributing money for 100 classrooms in rural Afghanistan, stressing education for girls and young women.[f]

Added to such individual works is the steady, although slow, progress of the European Union.

In addition to European accomplishments, German-American figures and phenomena started coming to the fore in the previous decade in the United States. The Max Kade Institute for German-American Studies, associated with university campuses, began its programming in the 1990s.[g] Probably the best-known author, who has supplied us with many works revealing the German-American view of twentieth century events, is university professor Ursula Hegi.[h] In 1998 Missouri Western State College published a study titled "The German Hyperinflation of 1923: A Seventy-Fifth Anniversary Retrospective."[i] The study sheds new light on long-forgotten reports revealing the aftereffects of actions among the European nations, France, Belgium, Great Britain, and Germany, as the latter's Mark plunged to 4.2 trillion to a U.S. dollar.

Thus, *Cross Currents: In the Wake of the Great War* is an invitation from the author to expand our global awareness and to move on to a more enlightened way of thinking, a more magnanimous way of living, a challenge to embrace more of our common humanity. Yes, it is important "never to forget," but it is also important that we do not point our youth, the next generation, toward the battlefield where the last military fracas left off, especially in the face of the escalating consequences of modern warfare. We fool ourselves if we fail to recognize that we are engendering ongoing hatred, thereby risking ever greater figures of annihilated innocents. The charge of the twenty-first century is to learn to live in peace with *all* peoples on this limited globe.

Photo taken in the village of Daisendorf in 1914 with the Ritsche farmstead in the background. From Left: Siblings Adolf, Theodor (with their mother Maria), Marie and Friedrich

PART ONE

"The Old Country" – Spring 1923

"America, thy lot is better." — Johann Wolfgang von Goethe

(Amerika, du hast es besser.)[1]

AMERICA OR THE ARGENTINE [2]

hen Friedrich came in from the barn for the mid-afternoon coffee break, Marie, Anna, Berta, and *die Mutter* looked up expectantly from their mending. Before he came in each day, Friedrich checked the mail at the entrance to their circle of farm houses in the village of Daisendorf. But his hands were empty again. His mother said, "*Ach ja, noch einmal nichts.*"[3]

Friedrich, who was in charge of the family farm, stamped his feet on the entry rug to remove the light dusting of snow from his boots. "If they would at least answer yes or no, we could get on with things."

Die Mutter looked at her son appreciatively. He too was getting exasperated. She knew, if they had two fewer mouths to feed, Friedrich would be under far less pressure.

"Come, have your coffee," she said, thinking—it's funny even though it's only a malt beverage of roasted grain and chicory, we still call it coffee. Poor Friedrich! He deserves real coffee, real bean coffee, that will give him a lift upon his return to the unheated barn, spending all winter repairing those farm implements and barn fixtures which have fallen apart during the growing season.

Friedrich poured milk, from which the cream had been skimmed, into the brown liquid. It gave the brew a dull grayish-blue color, not like pure cream, which turned coffee a rich shade of toast. The family used to keep a part of their dairy products for themselves, but most of them they now sent to the cooperative for people better off to enjoy.

When Berta brought her husband the sugar, she stopped to rub his shoulders a moment. Friedrich's muscles were taut yet drooping. His wife called to their tousle-haired towhead, using the Upper German dialect, *"Komm, Anni, es ist Kaffeepause."*[4]

"Coffee break, coffee break," the little one sang, as she approached the table.

Her aunt Marie sliced the last of a loaf of bread, while her other aunt, the older Anna, brought jam made from their own pears. The dark brown spread, flecked with spices, didn't substitute for butter, but it would do. Then the two sisters, in their early twenties, joined their brother Friedrich, their mother, and their sister-in-law Berta already at the table.

The family fell to their current topic of concern, that the mother's brothers, who had emigrated to America some twenty years before, might have decided against sponsoring their nephews, the youngest two in the family. It seemed as if so much time had elapsed since they had sent their request from the Old Country to Minnesota that they didn't know if they should give up and look for another solution.

"When did we send that letter?" Marie asked, as she got up to check on a batch of bread for supper.

"It was way last fall, September or October," the older Anna answered her sister before she went to the root cellar to fetch vegetables for the evening soup. She came back with a rutabaga, bunches of turnips and carrots, a clump of kohlrabi, an onion and some potatoes.

Their mother said, "It's almost March, and we haven't even gotten a Christmas greeting." She took out her hanky to wipe her face. *"Ja, vielleicht geht es ihnen doch nicht so gut."*

"But if it's not going so well in America, that would be unusual, *nicht wahr?"* asked Marie, her blond pony tail swinging back and forth as she fussed over the bread, deciding finally it was ready for the oven. Suddenly she stopped to pin up some loose strands, which were threatening to get too close to the heat.

"Ja, Mutter," Anna said. Her dark hair hung loosely down her back. "It would be unusual. Doesn't everyone do well in America? *Onkel Martin* has a prosperous farm, and *Onkel Anton* has a good job in town."

She began chopping the root vegetables. Then she added them to the liquid with the meager soup bone already simmering on the cast iron stove.

"That would say to me that they're doing well," mused Marie.

Berta commented, as she swooped up baby Heinrich,[5] perching him on one hip. "Didn't the American uncles each marry German emigrants, I mean, women, who had also arrived in America around the turn of the century?"

"Actually my brother *Anton* was already married." The mother bowed her head. "May *Tante Agnes* rest in peace."

The others replied, "Amen."

"*Ja*," the mother continued, "it's hard to believe she's gone two years already." They paused a brief moment remembering the arrival of the black-rimmed envelope denoting a death announcement, which Anton must have gotten from a German print shop in America. "*So jung!* Only forty-four. *Und mein armer Bruder,* left with three daughters. *Ja,* even America can't make everything right."

"But they must be grown by now and a big help. Both families wound up with three children, *nicht wahr?*" said Berta.

"That's true, but of the six, they all are girls except one," Friedrich mentioned, wiping off his moustache.

"Are you insinuating that girls can't do the work?" Anna demanded, giving her brother a hopeless look. "Who do you think stepped in while all the men were at the front?"

The question hadn't been quite fair. Although it was true that women had to take over for shopkeepers called to the front, many farmers like Friedrich remained in their occupation. But he let the utterance pass. After all, the women did do a great deal of the farm work.

Die Mutter interjected with her usual "*Ach ja.* Perhaps Martin and Anton too are suffering from the war's destruction."

"But the war was not fought on American soil," Friedrich reminded them, "so at least they aren't rebuilding." What could be the delay? Even if the American relatives had mailed their Christmas letter late, it should have arrived by now.

The mother sighed. *"Ach ja!"* The term "Oh, yes" was neutral, but somehow from the lips of the mother it was fraught with pessimism. "We can't wait too much longer if the boys are still to go this year. It takes time to make all the arrangements."

Berta, before she started upstairs with the baby to change his diaper, called back, "But they've always been so faithful in writing. A letter is sure to come soon."

The door opened and the two potential emigrants appeared. *"Onkel Adolf! Onkel Theodor!"* Little Anni's tone revealed her excitement at seeing her young uncles.

"Wie geht's dir, Anni?" The two recent arrivals, their cheeks still pink from the early spring wind, looked down at her blond head adoringly. "I'm fine!" Her face was tilted up to them, hands provocatively on hips.

"You're earlier than usual. Is something wrong?" Friedrich's voice quivered slightly as he observed his two youngest brothers. He thought—Adolf is almost twenty, Theodor eighteen. Are they really old enough for such a journey? Friedrich had to remind himself, if it had been a few years earlier, they would have been going off to war as soldiers, a war which had robbed many a young man of his early adult years and furthermore forced him into a society that during his absence had become alien to him. Returning soldiers at the village tavern often talked about their discomfort, but they were often countered with, "At least you came back."

Now Adolf assured his older brother, "No, we just finished the job we were working on." His next utterance betrayed his preoccupation. "Any letter?" And when someone said not yet, Adolf, his jaw tightly drawn, said, "A letter must come soon."

Theodor added, "Yes, we can't live on odd jobs around the countryside too much longer. The urgent jobs are drying up and people will just leave the rest for better times." His clear, white forehead showed the suggestion of a frown.

"Maybe we'll have to write to our brother Karl in Argentina," the two boys indicated. The thought had occurred to them lately as they walked the five miles or so between their village of Daisendorf and its nearest town of Meersburg, where most of their temporary jobs occurred. Of the two most popular places to which Germans emigrated in the aftermath of the Great War, the two adolescents preferred the American states to the Argentine. However, they couldn't exclude the latter altogether. Karl, the third youngest male in the family, had gone to the River Plate republic two years before, drawn by incentives the government offered to immigrants to add to its sparse population and its meager work force.[6]

They never forgot Karl's description of his introduction to the new land. The hotel where immigrants stayed while arranging their papers lay in the colorful Bohemian quarter of Buenos Aires near the harbor called La Boca. "Each structure," he wrote, "is brightly painted with a different color—aqua, magenta, yellow, chartreuse. Furthermore, sills and frames are outlined in contrasting colors, giving the harbor a look of eternal cheer and mischief." As a housepainter by trade, Karl seemed deeply impressed by the scene. It must have been a welcome sight, after the drab, unkempt appearance of the Old Country.

Most Argentine immigrants joined the gauchos on ranches in the pampas or chose life on smaller farms in the north, but Karl was drawn to the city life of the *porteños*.[7] According to his subsequent letters from Buenos Aires, he was doing well. The latest communiqué, in fact, was written on letterhead which included their surname and that of another, most likely his associate. It advertised any type of enhancement for house walls, from simple painting to wallpapering and wall-texturing, from imitation wainscoting and speckling to scallops and false ceilings.

Karl's success prompted the two youngest members of the family to reconsider a move to the South American country. "Look!" Theodor had summarized one day walking home with Adolf, "Karl,—well, now he calls himself Carlos—has done so well that he has already gone into business with someone in Buenos Aires." To have his own business, that was Theodor's dream, too, his own woodworking factory one day.

"Yes, and Karl would surely see us through to our own start," Adolf, an electrician, had ventured. Nevertheless, they were holding out for America. It definitely had the economic edge. Finally, a decision between the two countries proved unnecessary. A week later Friedrich opened their mailbox among the row at the entrance to their cluster farm village[8] to find an envelope with unfamiliar foreign stamps, as brightly colorful as the snow crocuses had been so recently as they poked their way through the light layer of snow. The letter was postmarked Eden Valley. That was the village where *Onkel Martin* and *Onkel Anton* had settled in Minnesota. Friedrich hurried toward the house with the treasure.

"Vati," his daughter Anni called upon seeing the colorful envelope, *"Hast du was für mich?"*

"Nein, I'm afraid I don't have anything for you, *mein Liebchen.* This is a letter *für die Oma aus Amerika."* Anni had certainly heard the words "from America" enough lately. Now she noticed the adults had stopped in the middle of their activities. Something important was happening. The three-year-old started to jump up and down. When two-year-old Heinrich saw his sister's glee, he too jumped up and down, clapping his hands at her.

"Hier, Mutter," Friedrich said, "the long-awaited letter. The postmark says January, but I can't read the date. If it was late January, it might be logical that it didn't arrive until now."

"Endlich," the mother cried, fondling the envelope before she opened it.

"At last," the two youngest sisters agreed. They all looked on anxiously, as the mother read through the letter. Would the mother come out with an *ach ja?* They waited. But there was no *ach ja.* That was a good sign. Finally they could contain their curiosity no longer. *"So?"*

The mother shook herself from her reverie. *"Nichts, alles ist in Ordnung!* My brothers in America are going to sponsor the boys!" She put her hand to her head in relief.

"Did you hear that, *Annerl?"* Friedrich asked, while Berta winced at the Swabian diminutive of southwest Germany that Friedrich preferred for his daughter. "Grandma says everything's all right! *Dein Onkel Adolf und dein Onkel Theodor fahren nach Amerika!"*

Anni shouted, *"Amerika, Amerika!"* and started dancing again, whereupon Heinrich resumed his clapping. "Uncle Adolf and Uncle Theodor are going to America!" Anni sang.

That evening the elder Anna and her sister Marie were sent to the local butcher's, a few doors away, for cold cuts which the family managed somehow despite the depression, to add to their usual supper of soup and bread.

The wind was already getting warmer, the girls noticed as they settled down on a roadside bench next to their field of fruit trees. Adolf and Theodor should be coming any moment from behind a pear tree. When the brothers finally appeared, the sisters rose to meet them, chanting, "Guess what! Guess what!"

"The pear trees are beginning to blossom?" said Adolf.

"No," the sisters sniveled. Marie threw up her arms, while Anna declared, "Much more important than that."

"No!" Theodor said. His facial expression had turned expectant. He looked at Adolf. "It can only be a letter from America, *richtig?*"

"Right!" said Adolf, beaming at their sisters.

"Ja, richtig!" the girls returned.

"And the uncles said yes!"

The girls eagerly nodded. "So, it's going to be America then?" The sisters waited for confirmation.

"Ja, gewiß!"

The sisters' expressions turned to relief. America was certain to be the wiser choice from what they knew of the government.

Theodor eyed the old leather satchel the family used for transporting food. "But why are you carrying the grocery bag?"

"Because we bought *Aufschnitt!*" his sisters said.

"We're going to have cold cuts tonight?" Adolf raised his eyebrows in surprise.

"Yes, to celebrate!" Anna waited for the surprise to sink in. Then she opened her money pouch. "But look at the bills we got in change."

Theodor took hold of the wad of paper money. There was even a 10.000 (10,000)[9] *Deutsch Mark* bill among them. He observed that the note had recently been printed. The date said February 1923. Theodor's imagination suddenly took flight. "Boy! Would I love to have one of those! Wouldn't it make a good conversation piece in America? Nobody would believe it. This is the price of a pound of butter."

"Or two pounds of meat." Adolf was anxious to add a more practical consideration.

There was a pause, contemplating the depression. Their two sisters were looking at their brother incredulously. Finally Anna asked weakly, "Our inflated money?"

"Oh, I know, I know," Theodor hastened to add, "You need every bill you can get."

"On the contrary," said Marie, who sensed the situation more realistically. "Tomorrow it may only be half the worth of today."

"*Richtig!*" Adolf added. "And after all this time with rising prices since the Great War there is no sign that the rate of inflation is bottoming out."

Marie shrugged. "You know what people are already saying. Our bills are not even worth the paper they're printed on."

1904, year of Theodor's birth

Samples of bills put out by various German-speaking states

January 1923

March 1923

December 1922

Samples of German-Marks: The bottom photo says Eine Milliarde Mark, which translates as one billion Marks. It is stamped in red over a previous bill for 1000 Marks to show its new worth.

Fifteen Mark stamp is overprinted with
400 thousand Marks.

This stamp is worth 10 billion Marks.

EPISODE TWO

BLIND RABBITS

𝒜 t supper that night, after Friedrich said the blessing, he passed the cold cuts to Adolf and Theodor first. "Here," he said, "you two, the youngest family members, are the honored guests tonight." The brothers' eyes lit up. It sounded as if there were no limitation on cold cuts!

When Anna brought from the root cellar their last bottles of *Weißherbst*, Theodor exulted, "Even white autumn wine!"

"*Ja*," said Anna, "we reserved it just for this occasion."

"*Na ja*," said Friedrich, "and not just wine from any white autumn grape, but from the *Meersburger Weißherbst!*"

"*Genau!*" Marie added, "our own local wine." One could see the vineyards stretch out where buildings didn't obstruct the view between Daisendorf and Meersburg. The sloping countryside between the two populations captured the sunrays all day long. The family owned some of the grape fields, along with their farm neighbors. The local wine cooperative supervised the wine industry, exercising careful control over the grape species and advising the best time to harvest.

Marie brought their *Römer* wine glasses, the ones with etched cups and green stems, acquired in better times. "I thought they were perfect for the occasion."

The mother nodded. When Friedrich had served everyone, he proposed a toast: "*Zum Wohl!*"

"And to your well-being also!" the family responded.

Friedrich continued, "To our uncles, Martin and Anton, in the New

Country and to our brothers, Adolf and Theodor, still in the Old, that the preparations for the trip in the next weeks be successful."

They raised their wine, took a sip, then saluted each other with their glasses. The small group fell to relating incidents about their American uncles, which Friedrich's wife initiated. "When did Martin and Anton go to America?" Berta asked.

"About twenty years ago," Marie answered. "*Richtig, Mutter?*"

The mother said, "That's right. Actually several of you weren't even born yet when Martin left. I don't remember the year exactly, but he went a number of years before Anton. I do remember," she indicated to Adolf and Theodor, "you two youngest were not yet here when Anton left."

The mother moved up the line in the family, pausing several times when her memory was taxed. "Anna, you must have been the youngest then, and you were still a baby. Karl and your brother Heinrich were but toddlers. Marie, you were not yet in school." Then she jumped to the older children. "Your husband," the mother turned to her daughter-in-law, "and the oldest member of the family, Josef, were preparing to farm, and their older sisters, Fanny and Emilie, were in vocational schools. So that leaves Otto, Hugo, and Sofie in the middle. That's thirteen, *nicht wahr?*"

"*Richtig, Mutter.*" Marie laughed. "Only I think I was already in school too."

"But why did your brothers go?" asked Berta. The large family's history was still a blur in her mind, though she had joined the family several years ago. With the imminent departure of her young brothers-in-law, Friedrich's wife was suddenly insistent on getting the details straight.

"Because they didn't have a future here," the mother said.

"But there was no war at the time," persisted her daughter-in-law. Then she thought she had better qualify the statement. "What I mean is, our country was not in ruins like it is today."

The mother shrugged. "But there was something else at stake. Martin had always dreamed of having a big farm. He thought his possibilities were greater in the 'Land of Opportunity'."

"You have to consider, Berta," added Friedrich, "that in this part of the country every child inherits a part of the parents' land."[10]

Berta laughed, shaking her head. "I really can't imagine dividing a farm thirteen ways!"

Theodor straightened in his chair. "Of course, long ago, when the custom was adopted, if a family had thirteen children, they rarely all made it to adulthood."

"*Jawohl!*" Adolf pointed to himself and Theodor. "As time goes on and babies don't die as often, the old law complicates inheritance for us."

The mother nodded. "You see, in Martin's case, he didn't inherit good farmland nor was there any suitable land for him to buy. And he had his heart set on farming. We family members decided among ourselves that rather than break up the farm into small parcels, we would draw up a settlement. Those members getting land would compensate those not inheriting it with a certain sum of money. When everyone arrived at an arrangement agreeable to all, we went to a lawyer who helped us with the papers."

The numerous non-adjacent farm fields Berta had encountered when she came to the area had always troubled her. Now she intervened before her mother-in-law could finish. "Oh, so you can do some negotiating."

"*Ja,* such a solution actually had become quite common by then," said the mother.

The brothers said, "That's what's happened in this family, too. Look how many members have already made their own way. More than half of us are gone from the homestead area."

The mother nodded again. "*Richtig!* Now Martin, with his cash allotment, was able to pay his expenses to America and even put a down payment on some land there."

Marie said, "But do you know what your challenge in the New Country is going to be? Language, just like for our uncles."

Suddenly the mother broke out laughing. "*Gewiß!* Remember the story about the rabbits?"

Friedrich slapped his knee as he glanced around the family. "Not too long after Onkel Martin left, a letter came for Onkel Anton, who liked to hunt. Martin wrote, *'Ja, komm mal 'rüber. Es gibt hier viele blinde Hasen.'*"

"Yes, come on over, there are lots of blind rabbits here?" Adolf echoed. He looked at Theodor incredulously. Neither seemed to have heard the story before.

"Remember how excited Anton got?' said the mother. "We wondered what in the world could cause so many blind rabbits in one location. But Anton thought only of the easy hunting. When he got over to America, the first thing he asked Martin was, 'Where are the blind rabbits?'"

"Onkel Martin's English, however, wasn't that good at the time," said Friedrich. "He finally had to admit that he had misunderstood. There was no such thing as blind rabbits."

"Ja," the mother piped up. "Apparently Martin had gone one day to their village of Eden Valley. You know, over there it isn't like here. The village and supplies are a long way from the farms, so they were not in constant contact with English. Besides, most of the village people didn't even speak English."

"They spoke only German?" intercepted Berta.

"Ja, well, most were recent German settlers just like Martin and Anton," said the mother.

"They hadn't learned English yet."

"At least the particular crowd that Onkel Martin overheard," said Friedrich, "was talking in English about the current rabbit population. Martin heard something that made him assume they were talking about blind rabbits. Afterwards, when he had learned more English, he realized they had said 'plenty rabbits,' not blind rabbits, but it was too late. Onkel Martin had already sent off his letter."

Theodor said, "Oh! 'Plenty' in English must sound much like *'blinde'* in German."

"Richtig!" said Friedrich. "Onkel Martin got a lot of teasing about that."

Die Mutter, whose full figure shook inside her ample clothing, chuckled. "But my brother Anton finally said to himself that plenty rabbits were almost as good as blind rabbits, as long as one had good aim."

After everybody had stopped laughing, Friedrich added, "Well, you're going to learn a lot of new ways there. For one, they have less stringent hunting laws. Not like here, where we need permission from the *Jägermeister*[11] to hunt. There, a hunting license is all you need, if that. *Ja*, Onkel Anton wound up very satisfied with the hunting opportunities in America."

"*Ach so*," *die Mutter* sighed as the evening wore on. "And I have never seen my brothers since." Her declaration suddenly made them realize that the same could happen with Adolf and Theodor. It brought a sudden note of gravity to the celebration.

Little Anni got out of her seat finally and approached her favorite uncles. She said, "*Aber keine Sorge*, Onkel Adolf, Onkel Theodor, we'll come visit you." She patted them both on their arms reassuringly and turned to her mother to say, "*Nicht wahr, Mutti?*"

But Berta could not bear to assure her little daughter not to worry, that America was too far away, *jawohl*, the distance would be unmanageable for them. It was hard enough for the family just to support its two youngest adults.

EPISODE THREE

BODENSEE BEQUEST

The child's suggestion awakened the family to the risk for its future emigrants. During the next few days the departure weighed on all of them as they thought about possible consequences of the trip. Moreover, the mood intensified whenever the family shared the boys' imminent departure with others. Everywhere they went, a long list of horror stories about the transatlantic trip assaulted them. Not only was the Titanic disaster eleven years earlier still fresh in their minds as the worst ocean catastrophe, but other tales about woeful previous crossings floated about, coating their hopeful prospects in a morose wrapping.

One evening, a number of their neighbors gathered at the local inn in Daisendorf. Farmer Bauer, his husky figure dominating the table, asked, "You know what the ships that cross the Atlantic are called?" He paused before bellowing, "Swimming coffins! Sickness develops easily in those close quarters. And then there are the rats."

His wife added, "*Ja, Mäuse!* The pesky brutes spill their droppings wherever they please, and they get into the food supply. I had a distant cousin who went over there in '95. He wrote that he woke up one night

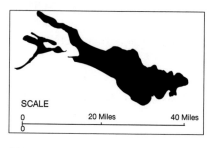

Outline of the Bodensee (Lake Constance in English.) The Rhine River flows into and out of the lake.

SCALE

0   20 Miles   40 Miles

with something scurrying over him. Sure enough, in the morning they discovered evidence of mice on the floor, and he was covered with scratches. He later died from something they call typhus. Only passengers don't call it that. They call it 'ship fever'."

The mention sparked the memories of others and a catalog of such stories ensued. "When my great aunt went, the trip took six weeks," said Innkeeper Wirth, "They had to 'bury' half the persons on board at sea because they starved to death." The story reminded Grocer Mittler of his great aunt. "She died in a measles epidemic on board. Up to one third never made it to the other side." Thereupon Barber Schnitzler replied, "One third! I think the usual statistics are more like two-thirds!"

"*Sicher*," said Teacher Lehrer. "*Aber noch etwas!*"

"What else?" inquired the guests.

"I hate to remind you of this, *meine Jungen*,"—when the teacher called Adolf and Theodor "my boys" like he did when they were still in school, a shot of nostalgia pierced them— "you're going to need much more English than you learned in school."

So they had heard, and another bevy of comments on the language ensued.

In Meersburg, they received more instructions. At a hotel where they occasionally delivered farm produce, Cook Koch looked down over his round belly, especially at Theodor's skinny figure, and advised, "Carry plenty of food, like crackers, salami, hard cheese. Even though by law ships now have to provide food, it doesn't always last the trip, especially if there's a storm and the trip takes longer than planned. Then people steal food from each other and fighting breaks out."

Secretary Schreiber at the courthouse, when the two applied for their passports, also had tips. "*Passen Sie auf!*" and the boys stood alert to her command. What was going to come next? "If you don't want your name changed when you get to Ellis Island, make sure they spell it right on your papers."

At the ticket office where they initiated their railroad and seafaring arrangements, Ticket-seller Schalter warned, "Get your money in as soon as possible. With the money situation the way it is . . . " The boys merely nodded. There was no need to go on.

When Doctor Arzt provided a general physical, the pitfalls of nutrition came up. "Take a few oranges," he advised. "They're an antidote against scurvy."

The family soon realized, however, that for the most part people were remembering tales of old in the days before steamships became common, before the enactment of a food provision law and the discoveries on nutrition, tales that nevertheless lingered on among the folklore. "They're just trying to help," the mother summarized finally.[12]

The horror stories, nevertheless, soon reappeared in another form. The value of the Mark had been plummeting ever since January. But now the jumps were not merely by hundreds, but by thousands, and then by tens of thousands, and the end was not in sight. Their town friends working in factories related how they were paid daily. They made their purchases on the way home before the Mark was further devalued. To wait until the next day was to risk losing purchasing power.

Carrying the paper money became so bulky that some citizens opted to transport it in wheelbarrows. The story was going around that a factory worker, arriving home too tired for the moment to deal further with the barrow, left it loaded in front of his house. When he went to retrieve it, he found the bills scattered by his doorstep with the wheelbarrow nowhere to be seen.

But hyperinflation[13] was to get even worse. One day soon thereafter Adolf and Theodor returned in late afternoon from Meersburg, where they had been delivering farm produce in exchange for items the farm family could use. Adolf, anxious to report the latest status of the Mark, drew out for the family the case needed to hold all the inflated bills. "You should see what we got back in Marks for change." He began shuffling through them. It was worse than the time their sisters met them in the orchard and Theodor had wished for a mere 10.000 bill, which might have bought a pound of butter. Now it would take over 100.000 Marks.[14]

"Lots of them, *richtig?*" The mother continued her mending.

"Worse than that." Adolf drew out the bill he had apparently been looking for and held it up to the mother. "*Schau mal, Mutter.* It's not even printed on the back."

Unbelieving, she took another stitch and suggested, "Maybe they just missed it."

"*Nein, Mutter.* We've got more like this. That's what they're doing now."

"*Ja,*" Theodor backed him up. "They're saying there was no time to print the back."

"*Mutter,* it's no longer daily changes in the Mark's worth, but hourly!" said Adolf.

"*Um Gottes willen! Das ist ja Unsinn!*" The older woman had dropped her mending–needle and scissors clanking against the wooden floor–and slapped her cheeks with her hands.

"And look at this one," said Theodor, satisfied that they had at last gotten the mother's attention. "See, the new lower value is stamped in red right over the old value."

Now the younger women were alerted, repeating the mother's phrase, "For heaven's sake! That's nonsense, *lauter Unsinn.*" They paused a moment trying to let the "absolute nonsense" sink in.

Finally Marie exclaimed, "*Wirklich!* They've run out of time to print more money!"

"But when you stop to think about it, what difference does it make?" reminded Theodor. "It's not backed by gold anyway. Ever since runaway inflation started in January."

"*Ja,* when the French and the Belgians invaded the *Ruhrgebiet,*"[15] said Adolf dolefully. But the family knew that he was in part mourning the assassination of Walter Rathenau,[16] a member of the cabinet in the Weimar Republic. Adolf had begun following news items about his father, Emil, when he became head of the nation's electrical company. News of his son naturally followed.

The mother said, "Our miners in that industrial area responded by refusing to work."

"Well, our government encouraged passive resistance to Allied demands," Anna added.

Berta voiced the concern of them all. "Where is all this going to end?"

The family sat in silence for a moment trying to comprehend the implications for them.

"It's a good thing we live on a farm, or we would starve," Friedrich said finally.

"*Jawohl!* Things weren't even that bad in the city during the Great War!" Berta blurted.

Die Mutter bit her lip. She had lost her closest friend two years ago from complications caused by malnutrition,[17] despite the mother's attempts to supply her with food. When she finally learned of the diagnosis, it was too late to reverse the condition. But she was not alone. Everyone knew someone who had succumbed to starvation of nutrients.

After another pause Theodor spoke on a lighter note. "We'll soon be paying more for a glass of beer at the inn. The price has risen sharply. In town it's now 3.000 Marks!"

"*Für ein Glas Bier?*" Friedrich was horrified.

"For a single glass of beer?" Marie echoed.

"And before the Great War, it cost a mere thirteen pennies," the mother murmured.

The boys continued. "And potatoes the same.[18] They're up to 2.000 Marks per pound."

Friedrich eyes widened to whitened circles. "*Kartoffeln! Das kann nicht sein.*"

"Potatoes?" gasped Marie. "*Du hast recht.* That can't be. Just last year they cost only eighty Marks per pound."

"*Ja,* and ten years ago, four cents." The mother's voice came through distant and eerie.

After a bit, Berta mollified, "Well, you just can't go to the inn as much," and she directed a teasing glance at her husband. However, he didn't accept the gesture.

"That's not it, *Liebling.* I mean beer has always been one of those commodities that seemed protected from higher prices. Up to now, its price has risen slowly by comparison. And potatoes? They're a staple. What are the city folk doing to stay alive?"

"*Richtig!* Potatoes are not like butter or meat, after all," Anna said.

Finally the mother, trying to match Berta's attempt at humor, said, "I just hope you two boys didn't buy any beer in town." Then suddenly reversing her mood, she grabbed her two youngest, pulling them tightly to her. She had already lost Karl, now Adolf and Theodor, too?

A few days later, Theodor boarded the ferry for Konstanz, the German city across the Bodensee[19] that was almost completely surrounded by the country of Switzerland. He was going to deliver some baby clothes they had obtained through bartering some of their farm produce to his sister Fanny who lived there. In her late thirties, she was now expecting her first child.

Theodor was also going to deliver his apprenticeship project, a carved box with an inlaid ivory lock, to the district office in Konstanz for appraisal. At his master teacher's, they had spent some time surrounding the box with the baby clothes designated for Fanny to pad Theodor's "masterpiece" against dents and scratches. Over the entire package they wrapped a scrap of woolen blanket.

An hour later Theodor stood at the rail of the ferry, regarding Konstanz in the distance. The city lay at the uttermost point of a peninsula jutting into Lake Constance, as the *Bodensee* was called in English. The scene before him emoted peace and calm. The *Konzilgebäude*[20] where John Huss was tried for heresy, was just becoming visible on the shore. The seagulls sailed overhead, the lake was hardly ruffled. Theodor didn't know he was about to hear what turned out to be the most threatening horror story so far.

It happened when Theodor, in his usual gregarious way, began talking with an attendant, also alongside the rail, who apparently had a few free moments. He told the attendant the motives for his trip today, indicating his package. He told him how he was anxious to know the results on his project, as he needed a favorable commendation to take with him to America.

"*Gewiß, Amerika,*" the attendant exclaimed. More information was exchanged. Then he broached the subject that had immediately come to his mind, when he heard the word *Amerika*. "Have you gotten your tickets yet?"

Theodor said they were waiting to hear from the ship companies.

"Well, in that case, I should to tell you before you buy, avoid getting steerage tickets."

Theodor pricked up his ears for that's what they had been looking for, since they were the cheapest.

His companion continued. "You know what steerage[21] is, *nicht wahr?* It's that place between deck and motor room where all the dingy engine smoke gets trapped. I've heard of too many persons who afterwards get lung problems from the bad air."

Theodor, nonplussed, pursued, "Why don't they just go up on deck for fresh air?"

"Because first-and second-class ticket holders object to the 'malodorous bodies,' as they put it, of those who can afford only a third-class ticket. For ship companies it's important that their primary customers are happy, so they confine steerage passengers to their quarters. With all the smoke, which, by the way, gets even worse when mixed with damp sea air, many travelers develop coughs right away. Others may not get anything until later."

"*Wirklich?*" Of all the roaming rumors, this one had never come up.

"But those with weak lungs before they even board ship are the worst off. In fact, some by the end of the trip have a good case of tuberculosis, and you know what that means."

Theodor braced himself. "They're sent back?"

"*Richtig!* But don't worry," the attendant said, appraising his listener's slender figure. "You look pretty healthy to me."

Theodor reflected briefly, although my eye's been bothering me a lot lately.

"Nevertheless, I wouldn't take a chance. You don't want to wind up like the one in the *Ritt über den Bodensee.*" He saw that he drew a blank with Theodor. "You must have heard that poem by Gustav Schwab. Everybody's got to read the local authors in school."

"*Selbstverständlich!* I do know it."

The attendant nodded. "Remember the traveler in the poem? He took a ride over the Bodensee in the dark, not realizing until after dawn that he had safely survived a lot of dangers. Then he died from shock."

"*Das ist ja toll!*" Theodor responded to the crazy outcome.

Theodor accomplished his errands in Konstanz, delivering his prized box and spending some time with his ballooning sister. All the while, however, he couldn't wait to get home to tell Adolf the attendant's story. He found his brother at the edge of the commons in Daisendorf. "It's good we didn't buy our tickets yet."

"*Warum?*"

Theodor relayed the information he learned on the ferry. "Have you got strong lungs, Adolf?"

"*Ich weiß nicht.* But I do know we don't have extra money for first-or second-class."

"*Stimmt's.* But we also don't want our money to go for nothing."

Adolf shrugged. "I suppose not. We'll have to see what our choices are."

"*Ja,* we don't want to wind up like the one in the ride over the *Bodensee* . . . "

The ghost that dwells in the Old Castle

EPISODE FOUR

"DO LIKE THE SUNDIAL. . . . "

The snow crocuses had long ago retreated. The tulips and daffodils had come and gone, and the fruit trees had shed their blossoms to be replaced by fruit buds. The grapevines were forming tiny green clumps of beads where flowering sprigs once clung. The peonies were in full bloom for Pentecost.[22]

Departure time was getting closer. As they tended the crops, Adolf and Theodor would say one to the other, "*Denk mal!* We won't be here for the harvest." And the other would reply, "*Genau!* Just think! We'll be in America then," whereupon the former would mimic, "Exactly!"

Finally the time came for Theodor to pick up his precious box in Konstanz. He also wanted to stop in at Fanny's. But the excitement to know his test results drew him first to the district office. When he saw the papers, he knew he had to visit his *Meister*[23] on the way home as well. *Ja, der Herr Meister* Buchmeier should be the first to know.

But before leaving Konstanz, he stopped at his sister's. Theodor was surprised when Fanny's husband opened the door at their apartment. "Good news," he told his brother-in-law. "Fanny gave birth to a girl last night." That meant a trip to the hospital where mother and daughter were doing well. Theodor's sister was lying in bed with his pink-wrapped niece in her mother's arms. His older sister was looking strangely younger than the last time he had seen her. "We've named her Hildegard," said Fanny.[24]

On the ferry some time later, Theodor thought, how nice had been the visit. Despite the difference in age, Fanny had always been close to him and Adolf. Even today she came through for her little brothers. She sent some money, salvaged from her seamstress' income, with them for the America trip.

But now he must stop at his *Meister's* in Meersburg, although it meant a delay in getting home. His teacher should be the first to know the outcome of his apprenticeship tests. When Theodor pulled the cord to the bell pole at his *Meister's* house, the three years he had roomed and boarded there during his apprenticeship flashed through his mind. His stay began right after his graduation from eighth grade, when he was fourteen, the year the Great War ended.

The door opened suddenly and there stood the *Meister's* wife, the one who had fed him and washed his clothes all the time he had lived there. "*Theodor!*" she exclaimed. "*Sehr schön, dich zu sehen.*" The way she said it made Theodor feel she was sincerely glad to see him. She looked at his load knowingly, but kept her silence. The honor of unshrouding the outcome belonged to her husband. "*Komm! Der Herr Meister* is in the cabinet shop with his apprentices."

Upon glimpsing Theodor in the doorway, the *Meister* skipped the usual greeting. "*Der Kasten!* You've got back the box!" He approached his former student with arms outstretched to relieve him of his load. "Let's see it once more!" He stepped to the side while Theodor uncovered his endeavor.

"Look at that piece! Isn't it something to be proud of?" The *Meister* was speaking in part for the benefit of the four apprentices, who he knew, although his back was turned, had paused in their tasks to survey the visitor. "So, tell me, what did they say? No, don't tell me, I already know by the expression on your face. You passed with flying colors."

Indeed, Theodor's face was beaming as he produced the papers. "I see," the *Meister* commented slowly after he had read through the documentation, "not good grades—", he paused to see if his wife was still there and if the apprentices were paying attention,"—but outstanding ones." He threw his hands up in a gesture of excitement. "But then, that's what I would have expected."

Theodor was communicating some of the exchange in the district office, when one of the apprentices needed the *Meister's* attention. In the interim Theodor's eyes became riveted on his old workbench, which had all of its tools in place, just like he had left them, awaiting a new apprentice. Finally, Theodor couldn't resist stepping closer. The vise attached to its edge had its handle poised to turn. Hammer, saw, chisel, screwdriver, plane all hung neatly in a rack above the bench. Its surface was marred and scarred from years of use. Cuts from the chisel and dents from the slip of the hammer decorated the top in some unfathomable design. Even the saw marks on the corners looked as if they might be part of a decorative frame.

He opened a drawer to find the set of carving tools he had used on the box. They were lined up in progression from large to small. The largest one served to carve indentations, leaving a sculpture in a recessed background. The smallest one made possible finer details, like grooves in leaves and angles on flowers. The awl, used to form mottled backgrounds, was also there, as was sandpaper of varying grades. He had spent some time with a master carver, a start to the fulfillment of journeyman status.

After a bit, the *Meister's* wife, who had disappeared momentarily, addressed them. "It's *Kaffeepause*. Maybe you will want to take your break in the parlor." Turning to Theodor, she stated, "You will surely have coffee with us, won't you?"

"*Gewiß, gnädige Frau.*" Theodor made a slight bow, with a tiny tinge of guilt toward those waiting for him at home. But then he also remembered it would be real coffee—how he had longed to taste real coffee. The last time she had invited, he had been here with Adolf. Theodor was about to accept, but his brother had been faster. "No thanks. Mother will be waiting for us at home with coffee." Then Theodor could only mumble helplessly, "*Ja, danke nicht, Frau.*"

As the *Geselle*[25] and *Meister* left the workshop, the latter addressed his apprentices, "*Lehrlinge*, I'll be back shortly. Why don't you apprentices take your break in the meantime too?" Theodor thought they would probably be having their *Butterbrot*. The *Meister's* wife had never scrimped on so-called luxury items like butter.

In the parlor the *Meister* inquired, "You're surely going to take the box along to America?"

"*Gewiß!* But I don't know exactly how. It's awkward to carry I've found and, of course, I don't want to see it scratched or chipped." The district office had given him some padding to replace the baby clothes he had used when he delivered the project to them.

"*Sicherlich nicht.* I'll tell you what you need." Theodor slanted his head inquiringly. "A trunk. You could make one in the workshop, if you want. Do you have time before you leave? It would probably take only a week."

"Well, our dates are not yet fixed."

"Well then, it's settled."

When they went back to the shop to retrieve the box, the *Meister* surprised him. He snatched the hammer from above his old workbench. "Here, do you have room for a hammer? This one that you've worked with these past few years I always thought was just made for you." Embarrassed, he added, "You must have something from the shop, something to remember us by." Theodor had to admit the *Meister* had "hit the nail on the head" there. Still, he had never expected it, since the tool was new by comparison with the other tools. He had nonetheless often thought how nice was its heft, how snugly it fit in his hand, how his fingers easily followed the curve of the handle. He turned to embrace his master teacher and noted that he was not the only one with damp eyes.

After a few more exchanges, he prepared to leave. The *Meister* walked to the door with him and suddenly detained him with a hand on his elbow. Theodor turned to look at him. The *Meister* said, "*Du wirst es sehr gut in Amerika schaffen. Du hast soviel Ehrgeiz, Begabung, Geschicklichkeit.*" He took out his handkerchief to pass over his eyes.

Theodor left him, waving his handkerchief in farewell until he rounded a corner. The *Meister's* best wishes oscillated in Theodor's eardrums: "You will make it good in America. You have so much ambition, talent, ingenuity." The words had melted over him like a benediction.

He barely noticed his surroundings on his way home. Suddenly he was aware that Adolf stood before him by the chapel at the entrance to their community. "*Aber der Kasten, mein Bruder.* Here, let me relieve you. You've been carrying the box all the way from the ferry landing through the whole city of Meersburg. That's a long way."

Theodor nodded. "It's not heavy, it's just awkward." Theodor turned into the commons, when Adolf suggested they spend a moment in the chapel, which was always open.

"*Natürlich, eine gute Idee!* All in all, we have much to be thankful for!"

After a few moments, Adolf said, "Let's go to the house now. *Mutter* is so anxious to see the box. By the way, our sister Emilie arrived this afternoon."

In the entryway the family had gathered round before Adolf could set down the load. Emilie came from another room. "*Tag, Schwester Schwester!*" Theodor exclaimed as they embraced. "This is unexpected."

"Unexpected, maybe, but timely I see." She had already shed her nurse's uniform to keep it crisp and clean for the return trip to

Chapel in Daisendorf

Ludwigshafen, where she worked in a hospital. When Emilie was smocked in the long, dark, cotton dress of her profession, with her nurse's cap propped on her head, people on the street would nod, greeting with her nurse's title, *Schwester*, and they would grant her courtesies, such as insisting that she precede them in line.

Theodor remembered their mother's recent comment, that their "sister sister" had spent her whole adult life so far nursing soldiers, first at the front in the Great War and now the veterans in a rehabilitation ward. Theodor noted that although she was only in her thirties, her dark hair was losing its sheen and her skin was turning leathery.

In the tiny space that served as the sitting room, Theodor was hailed by all their neighbors in Daisendorf. Now he was embarrassed. He did not know that the whole community was going to be there. He excused himself. "*O weh,* sorry I'm late. I stopped at my *Meister's* house in town to let him know right away the results of the box."

"*Selbstverständlich!*" There was a murmuring that it was obvious the teacher had a right to know. Theodor didn't mention that his wife had invited him for *Kuchen und echten Kaffee.* That the cake was an expensive *Schwarzwälderkirschtorte* and the coffee real they didn't need to know either. Theodor's mouth was still watering from the chocolate cake put together in layers with whipped cream and cherries and laced with black cherry liqueur.

But Adolf whispered that there was another reason for stopping in the chapel. The farm community wasn't going to assemble itself until Theodor's arrival. Thus, Adolf had been posted there as sentry. During their time in the chapel, the villagers had rushed to their house.

Someone finally called impatiently, "*Um Gottes willen!* Unwrap the box!"

That drew Theodor to attention. "Wait, there's something else. Fanny is using the clothes we gave her."

The mother managed only her daughter's name. "Franziska?"

"*Ja, Mutter, du bist wieder Oma.*"

The mother clapped her hands. "I'm a grandma. I'm a grandma."

"But you've always been a grandma," insisted Anni.

The adults laughed and explained the situation to her.

"*Junge oder Mädchen?*" someone asked.

"A girl."

Emilie said to Anni, "*Du hast eine neue Kusine. Und sie heißt Hildegard.*"

"I have a new cousin and her name is," Anni paused before saying slowly, "Hil-de-gard."

As Theodor began to unfold his apprenticeship project from its woolen covering, the crowd quieted. When the *Lehrstück* was fully exposed, they praised the piece's sheen, its intricacy, its appropriateness. Then his sister Anna clamored to know what he had been graded on.

Theodor jumped into the long procession of requirements he had to fulfill for his apprenticeship test. He had to show on the box how well he could fit the edges together with no overlapping, that the lid fit snugly into the box's lip, that the hinges were mounted flush into the box's edges, that the inlaid ivory lock was evenly recessed. After that he had to prove his prowess with carving tools. The whole piece was decorated with a garden motif of vases, leaves, and flowers. And finally he had to show how evenly he could stain the wood, for although the dark brown box looked as if it were walnut, its wood was really oak. He pointed to the sides. On the one he had whittled his initials, T.R., and on the other, 1923, the year of his admittance to journeyman status. "When I started the carving I didn't realize that the year would also be my year of emigration."

"*Doppelt hält besser.*" Farmer Bauer shifted back and forth on his big feet, and Innkeeper Wirth added, "*Jawohl!* Double-checking never hurts."

"And where did you get the ideas?" asked Marie.

"*Aus den Büchern.*"

"From books?" Marie echoed.

"*Jawohl!* I spent a long time paging through books, a while back already. Ideas came to me gradually. I just couldn't think of what the object should be except I wanted something useful, not just a decorative piece. When talk of the trip came up, I thought, it must also be portable. A chair or a table wouldn't do. It had to be an item I could carry in case we went to America. That's when I decided upon a box, and what could be more appropriate than one to hold documents?"

"*Natürlich, ein Dokumentkasten!*" said Barber Schnitzler.

Marie nodded.

"*Das ist ja praktisch,*" Emilie said. "Not only indeed practical, but also clever." She brushed a finger lightly over the top, where Theodor had carved an inscription:

> *Tu' es wie die Sonnenuhr,*
> *Zähl' die heiteren Stunden nur.*

"Whatever made you choose that saying?" she asked.

"'Do like the sundial, count only the sunny hours?' I ran across it in a book when I was looking for ideas and I liked it."

But now Emilie had a chance to observe him more closely. "What's wrong with your eye? It's so red."

"Nothing, it's just sore," Theodor insisted.

Theodor's box showing top with message and side with 1923
the completion year of his apprenticeship

But Anna chimed in. "Marie and I were wondering about that, Emilie."
"Let me see it." Emilie lifted his eyelid. "I think we had better do something about that. It doesn't look like anything serious now, but if it isn't cleared up before you board ship, it might get worse." Funny, thought Theodor, second time I've heard precautionary words today. "Tomorrow I'll pick up some eye ointment at the druggist."

Emilie, thought Theodor, my other older sister, always taking care of us.

That night as Theodor was falling asleep, his mind reviewed the events of the day—the favorable comments on the box, the advent of a new member to the family, the care extended by his oldest sisters, his *Meister's* words, *die Frau Meister's* invitation for coffee break with the real brew and the region's most conspicuous contribution to the dessert file, Black Forest cherry cake. In addition there was the neighbors' congeniality and the family support. It had been a great day! It filled Theodor with resolve—I'm going to be the best immigrant I know how. I'm going to count only the sunny hours. And I'll have my box as a constant reminder.

EPISODE FIVE

SCHWABENLAND[26]

The following day at breakfast Emilie said, "Get me caught up! How's everything going with the trip?"

"I must say, despite the country's unstable state of finances," said *die Mutter*, "we've gotten together a nice sum of money for the boys' trip. And that's because so many family members have chipped in."

Emilie said, "*Wunderbar!*"

"Yes, Emilie, we haven't had a chance yet to thank you for your contribution!" said Adolf.

"*Das macht mir nichts aus.*"

"'Don't mention it.' That's what everybody says," said Theodor. "Adolf and I just hope that none are digging into their pensions."

In order not to betray herself, Emilie brushed it off by saying, "*Keine Sorge!* There's talk at this point that we should not rely on our pensions anyway."

Anna asked, "You think that people should be worried about their retirement money?"

Emilie frowned. "I hope things never get that far."

"It sure doesn't pay nowadays to have a savings account in the bank," said Friedrich.

"*Ja, stellt euch vor,*" commented Emilie.

"Well, then, Emilie, imagine this!" Marie wore her blond hair loose today. "*Mutter* has managed to put in an amount for the boys from her egg money."

The two youngest sisters contorted their faces into an expression of "Can you believe?"

Friedrich laughed. "Apparently no one knew that she has always put money aside from her egg sales, ever since Dad died in 1910."

"*Ach ja*, before that, Friedrich, before that," the mother confessed.

"That's fair," said Berta. "She takes care of the chickens and collects the eggs."

"*Gewiß!*" said Adolf.

"*Aber natürlich*, I don't sell many eggs these days. Just to some hotels. Otherwise, they go for bartering, not for cash."

Friedrich observed, "Sadly, that's what you do under the present economy."

"*Ja*, that's why when money comes in, we immediately apply it somewhere," Anna said.

The mother said, "I didn't mention your brother Hugo in the Black Forest yet. He sent a sum he said was extra from an order at the sawmill, one he didn't expect. Your sister Sofie and husband Lorenz have promised to send something from their beauty salon."

"That reminds me." Theodor dug into his pocket. "Fanny sent some money from her seamstress income, or so she said anyway." A look of incredulity went around the table as Theodor plunked the money on the table.

"I expect we'll hear from Heinrich and Otto, who haven't even answered yet," the mother concluded.

"And what about Friedrich and Berta?" Emilie was teasing Friedrich, with whom she had run around the farm as a toddler.

Marie spoke quickly, "Oh, they're going to provide transportation to the railroad station."

Friedrich felt obliged to explain. "*Ja*, like I say, we have no money, just the farm."

"Does that mean you've not been setting anything aside like a good Swabian?" Emilie taunted.

"I'm afraid," the mother intervened, "that Swabian thriftiness has gone by the wayside for many." It was true. All their penurious practices were vanishing in the postwar trauma.

"*Ja,*" Friedrich said, "I guess you'll have to send us to Scotland, *nicht wahr,* Berta?" Everyone laughed at the standard comparison of frugality—if you weren't thrifty enough here in *Schwabenland,* you were banished to *Schottland.*

Finally Emilie said, "I have to get to the druggist for Theodor's eye ointment. Then Marie and I talked about taking the ferry to Konstanz. Being this close I have to take advantage of seeing my new niece."

Anni spoke up. "*Meine neue Kusine Hildegard.*" From how smoothly the words came out it was obvious that the child had been practicing.

"*Sehr gut, Anni,*" Marie looked directly at her niece. "And I'm going to Fanny's because she needs help washing Hildegard's diapers and sterilizing her bottles."

Marie stayed on at Fanny's, but Emilie returned to Daisendorf that evening, because she had to leave for Ludwigshafen the next day.

Her visit left the family pondering some of the issues that had come up. Could matters get any worse? The Mark was still plunging. Savings accounts were being wiped out left and right. The irony was that Friedrich, in his failure to put money aside, might be the one to come out ahead in the end. The possibility of people losing their pensions was not far-fetched.

Die Mutter did not need to worry, for she would always be well taken care of on the farm. Yet lately she was not handling conditions well, seeing others suffer on top of the loss of her country's prestige.

Those in her circle of friends, who could look back upon a longer span of history, tended to see the end of the last century as the good old days. The older generation lamented how close they had come to standing among the great nations of Europe. They began resorting to nostalgic statements, such as, "If *Kanzler Bismarck* could only see now what has happened to all his social legislation,[27] he would turn over in his grave." They especially bemoaned the short life of their country, which unlike important European countries, was first united in 1871 under Chancellor Bismarck. That unification, which they felt he had accomplished, had not lasted even a mere fifty years. His importance began to loom ever greater in their eyes.

For the mother, such thinking too often carried over into her personal life lately. "*Ach ja,*" she said, using her favorite expression whenever she was reminded of the imminent departure of her youngest offspring. "First Karl, and now Theodor and Adolf."

One day little Anni even found her grandmother crying. In the older woman's hands was the family portrait. All thirteen children were present, some blond, some brunette, the girls with pompadours, the men with moustaches, all with stern faces and erect posture, except for the two youngest, doubled up in their chairs. Adolf must have been six and Theodor almost five. They sat relaxed, as if caught in some squirmy

Ritsche family portrait, 1908, Theodor seated left and Adolf right of the table.

position, a slight indication of impatience on their faces. Two years later their Papa died, she thought sadly.

Anni ran to the others in the kitchen. "*Warum weint die Oma?*"

The women said, "Grandma's crying because she is sad about our country, and because our family struggles so. That's why your uncles are leaving soon for America, to find work."

"*Onkel Adolf und Onkel Theodor?*" the blond cherub asked. It was beginning to sink in that going to this New Country, making *Oma* cry, was far more ponderous than she had thought. The mother would come out of one of these sessions significantly depressed, and when the family tried to console her, she merely persisted. "*Ja,*" she would say, "all the things in our past, of which we have been so proud, what good are they doing us now?"

The brothers, too, were going through a period of uncertainty, theirs centering on abandoning the family, yet welcoming a better life. Moreover, for a long while they were going to be without family except for each other. In his wistfulness, Theodor's thoughts suddenly wrenched him to a similar heartbreaking feeling in the past, the day his father died. His siblings had gone to work in the fields that day, thirteen years ago. But he, the youngest and only six, not yet strong enough for the day's work, was to stay home and take care of their ailing father. Suddenly Theodor found his father coughing wretchedly. Theodor cried out helplessly, but there was no one to hear. With difficulty, he got his arms around his father's frail frame and began rocking him. Suddenly his father's body gave a lunge so violent that he fell back out of Theodor's arms. The older man's throat emitted a sound Theodor had never heard before. Then he was still. Theodor remembered vividly his blanched, contorted face. It confronted him every so often in a weak moment.

But it was best not to think of such things now. It was bad enough realizing they were leaving the whole family. Worst of all, he realized that Marie and Anna would like to have joined them on their American venture. Like many young people, going to America had been on the minds of the young sisters since the end of the Great War. Most of their adult life had been spent in its deprived backdrop, with continual shortages of food, restrictions on their movement, and inadequate educational opportunity. Being slightly older, they had it worse perhaps, because even at their young age, they were more in a position to compare life before the Great War than their youngest brothers. To the sisters, going to America was awesome instead of frightening. However, they knew it was hard enough to scrape together transportation costs for two people.

One day in mid-summer, Adolf and Theodor made one of their usual trips of late to Meersburg to deliver farm produce in exchange for items they didn't produce on the farm. They returned from Meersburg in late afternoon to find everyone at the table for *Kaffeepause*, except Berta and the little ones. "*Keine Kinder?*" The brothers looked around, missing their usual clamor, as if they were trying to scare away demons of old with their noise. It was moments like these when it dawned on them, if they missed them now, what was it going to be like in America?

Quickly they turned their attention to the matter at hand. They had left with the grocery satchels filled with eggs, early potatoes and other root crops, a slab of meat and some chickens, some soup bones, lettuce, radishes and early onions. They had brought them to their acquaintances in town in exchange for other items. Now they took from one of the satchels sugar, flour, salt, a package of barley beverage, a couple cans of herring, and bath and laundry soap. Of course, some items they didn't need, but they could be further traded for ones they did need.

They also got a new harness. "Not exactly new," Theodor hastened to explain, "but better than the old one which will soon go *kaputt*."

"What's in the other satchel?" the mother asked.

"More clothes," said Adolf.

"*Ja*, underwear for our trip," said Theodor. "We traded some chickens for it."

Their audience couldn't suppress a laugh. Despite the ridiculous lengths to which they were sometimes driven, they somehow could always manage a bit of good humor.

The new consignment of clothes reminded the women that Theodor had not yet tried on the suit he was to inherit from Adolf. The older brother had worn it earlier when he was interviewing for electrician jobs. His brother Heinrich had passed it on to Adolf, but since then the latter had filled out too much to wear it. Luckily Heinrich had another suit to pass on to Adolf, one which he in turn had outgrown.

Although the women had expected some alterations to the suit in question, they were dismayed when they saw how loosely it hung on Theodor. They shook their heads as they pinched the fabric to see how sleeves or waistline might look if altered on the boy's delicate frame. Finally the mother gasped. "It will never do to go to America."

His sisters agreed. "*Stimmt's, das geht nicht!* Even taken-in it's going to hang on him."

But the problem was soon solved. The women kept bringing up the subject among their friends. Finally a neighbor remembered a suit her son had worn at his confirmation. "You know, Fritz, the one who never

Heinrich and Maria Ritsche, parents of Theodor and Adolf.

came home from the front." When she brought the suit to them, among the bundle were also a shirt and a tie. She was about to explain something, then left wordless.

Theodor felt strange inheriting a war victim's clothes. He recalled Fritz growing up in the farm community as a lively adolescent. Theodor got to know Fritz better because he had helped him with German grammar. In fact, he had helped many younger pupils with their schoolwork. A sentence he had recently read burst upon his mind, that all the talk of sacrifice for the war became convoluted into soldiers saying, "Hell! We are the sacrifice!" But in the end, Theodor knew, time was getting short before the trip. Besides, as a good Swabian, practicality ruled.

EPISODE SIX

MEERSBURG AM BODENSEE[28]

Despite being busy with farm work, Adolf and Theodor felt they spent much of the interim waiting—mostly waiting for their papers and waiting to hear from steamship companies about tickets, timetables, and prices. Early on they realized that it was going to take effort to coordinate the timing for all the phases of the trip. They had to settle the ocean voyage before they could arrange their train tickets to Bremerhaven, their port of departure on the North Sea. But finally they could notify their uncles in Minnesota to go ahead on the last step, the American leg of the trip, which the uncles had agreed to pay for.

Two days before departure, Adolf and Theodor made their last trip to Meersburg. They needed to pick up their tickets and the trunk still at the *Meister's,* as well as take care of the mother's last-minute errands.

It was also their last delivery of farm produce. They went to the *Wilden Mann* and other hotels and inns along the lakeshore. From windows overlooking the water, guests could view the panoramic beauty of the harbor. Finally, with empty satchels swinging at their sides, Adolf and Theodor greeted acquaintances along the road who wished them well, saying they would "press their thumbs together."[29]

As they made their way to the ticket office, the young men paused a moment on the *Seepromenade.* Grown-ups rested on benches

Meersburger shield composed of a lake (Meer) and a castle (Burg)

49

overlooking the water, while children leaned over the lakeside railing until they could see their reflections in the smooth surface. "*Vorsicht!*" cautioned a caretaker to a child challenging its safety by leaning over the railing too far. When Adolf and Theodor came out of the ticket office, they stopped to honor the significance of the moment. "This is it, Adolf! Do you realize? We did it!"

"*Jawohl!* We have our tickets! A year ago at this time, did we think this was possible?"

"Never!" Theodor took a big breath of fresh air. "And now we are taking our last stroll through Meersburg on Lake Constance."

The brothers turned around to view the land and spent the next few moments in silence, as if trying to imprint upon their minds forever their childhood landscape. The narrow band of flat earth containing the lakeside walk and a narrow street that butted up against the abrupt rise of the bluff was called the *Unterstadt*, the Lower Town.

From the lake, *die Meersburg*[30] dominated the town's panorama, even though only the upper portion of the massive structure showed above the foliage. Dating from A.D. 628, the "Fortification of the Lake" claimed to be the oldest, still-inhabited fortress in Germany. Its round towers, gables, thick walls, and slim openings to the world from which arrows had been released in all directions bespoke its medieval intention as a bulwark.

Rife with myriad legends and romantic tales about escapes and captures, the fortified castle boasted a secret door at lake level, where a narrow-treaded, covered stairway led up into the castle. Even if invaders found the stair entrance hidden among the foliage, they still had to permeate the narrow door, which was easily defended. In those days the bluff itself was almost impossible to scale. Its sharp angle to the sky and its thick vegetation virtually barred intruders.

A surge of nostalgia struck them then. Adolf asked, "Do you think America will have anything as picturesque as this? I hear its architecture is pretty uninspiring."

"*Ich weiß nicht.* But I can't help thinking, although we haven't seen much beyond here, that Meersburg has to be one of the most beautiful cities in Germany, if not in the world."

They fell silent again as they wondered how they would adjust to a world they felt would be lacking in history, but soon Adolf returned to reality. "We'd better get going. We have a lot to do." They walked to the one street inland from the harbor promenade. From there they went westward through the *Unterstadttor,* the Lower Town Gate, which intersected the *Steigstraße,* or appropriately, the Steep Street. This they easily climbed as they had so often, only today they were sure to take in each shuttered window along the route, each half-timbered façade called *Fachwerk,* and all the flower boxes filled with geraniums that brightened the dull, centuries-old stucco-like buildings—in short, some of the many characteristics that denoted Old Country style.

Halfway up the hill to the *Oberstadt,* or the Upper Town, *das Alte Schloß*[31] began to emerge. Before they reached the entrance to the narrow street leading to the Old Castle, they could hear the gurgling of its gigantic overshot mill wheel. For a moment they watched transfixed as the water poured down the trough and shot over cups mounted on the wheel's edge. They followed the hollow slats catching the water, whose weight drove the wheel downward. Upon turning into an upswing, the cups emptied their contents into the moat, before floating lightly onward. "I bet there won't be many of these mill wheels in the New Country," Theodor said.

Adolf had continued walking up the *Steigstraße,* only to find moments later that Theodor still stood entranced in front of the medieval mill wheel. All of a sudden Theodor's nostalgia took control. "Let's take a turn this way to the Old Castle," he called without looking around.

Adolf opened his mouth to object, but his nimble brother was already halfway up the incline. When Adolf caught up to him, he said, "Theodor, we've got to watch our time. We've still got things to do, *nicht wahr?*"

"*Jawohl,* but we won't take long." Theodor's eyes pleaded. "It's our last time, Adolf." In a twinkling he scampered onto the bridge that led across the moat. Then he stopped. At the entrance to the castle stood a watchman in a medieval costume. "Say," the latter called upon fixing his eyes on the two lads, "aren't you the young gentlemen who are going to America soon?"

"As a matter of fact, we're taking the train north to the coast day after tomorrow, *Herr Wächter*," they informed him.

"*Übermorgen. Wie schön!* I saw your picture in the newssheet." The watchman paused a moment. "I'll bet you'd like to see *das Alte Schloß* inside one last time." The brothers were about to back off, for they had no extra Marks for museums. But the watchman was already summoning the ticket seller inside. "How about it? Don't you think they deserve one last look on the house?" He disappeared a moment.

The brothers looked at each other. A free visit? Actually, most of the museum they had never seen. *Was für ein Glück!* Even Adolf warmed to the bit of luck.

"Remember when we used to deliver milk to the residents here as kids?" mused Theodor.

"*Ach ja!*" Adolf said, using their mother's favorite expression. "I was almost ten and you were about eight. That's ten years ago already."

"And remember the day you went by yourself and you tripped and milk spilled from the pails all over the road?" Theodor asked.

"*Ja,* you were sick that day, which meant I had to carry those heavy buckets all by myself. When the milk spilled all over the cobblestones, I thought I was in for it. But I got out of it."

"How? I don't remember that."

"I had to go back to the farm. There I persuaded *Mutter* and Innkeeper Wirth to give up their milk quota. It was a long morning. I had already eaten my two boiled potatoes, and all that walking left me hungry."

"*Ja,* that was the morning we did without milk for our coffee."

"Not only you. Also the lodgers in the castle. By the time I finally made the return trip, they had long before had breakfast."

But the watchman was already beckoning them to cross the bridge. Soon the brothers found themselves immersed in the age of chivalry. From every corner armor and cannons poked at them. Continuing into the Knight's hall, they examined chestplates, visors, helmets, lances

Annette von Droste-Hülshoff, for some, Germany's greatest poetess

and shields. After surveying the room, Theodor couldn't help uttering the oft-repeated phrase, "No wonder it took a crew of servants to dress them." The brothers peered through the narrow arrow slits in the towers. They climbed the steps inside the gabled Dagobert[32] Tower, a landmark by sea.

After a time, Adolf said, "We'd better get going now."

"Without seeing the rooms where our resident poetess lived when she came to town? *Mutter* is sending a book of her poetry for the relatives, don't forget. It would be a shame to tell our uncles over there that we never saw where she did some of her writing."

"*Ja, ja,*" Adolf conceded. "I suppose that's among Meersburg's attractions."

Satisfied, Theodor went into action. "*Das Fräulein Annette von Droste-Hülshoff*[33] talks about seeing the lake from her tower window, so her rooms must be facing south." They wandered a bit until they found the right hall. "*Großartig!* There's her name on that sign!"

A cozy, comfortable yellow-striped wallpapered room broke the bleak, blighted blotches of those parts of the castle still in their original state. "I wonder if she had a hand in furnishing her quarters?" Theodor scurried around the room examining the carving on bedboard, night table, and dresser.

"*Ja,* it looks like something that was done about the time she lived seventy-five years ago." Adolf stopped to read a sign in small print, which caused him to step quickly back. Just as quickly recovering, he said, "This is her death chamber."

Undeterred, Theodor said, "But the apartment goes on through that door over there." They were drawn to the funnel of light beyond and found a turret room brightly painted in a russet shade. It was labeled her study.

"No narrow defense slits here," observed Adolf. A great section had been gouged from the thick wall to accommodate an expanse of windows adorned with leaded glass.

"This must have been a wonderful room in which to work." Theodor turned himself around to see the whole room. "The southern exposure means sun all day long, just like with our *Weißherbst* vineyard."

"*Ja,* as long as it's not cloudy." Adolf had approached the windows, one of which was open. "Look at the magnificent view *das Alte Schloß* commands of the Swiss Alps."

Theodor joined him. "*Ja,* and the *Bodensee* between Germany and Switzerland."

"I'll bet the view of the *Meersburg* from the Swiss side is just as impressive." Adolf read the card next to the window. "'*Es glänzt wie die Meersburg*'—Swiss saying."

"It shines like *die Meersburg.*[34] You know what, Adolf? That proverb must have originated before the New Castle was built in the 1700s. Because I don't think it was until then that people would have switched from calling it the 'Lake Fortress,' to calling it the Old Castle."

"*Jawohl!*" agreed his brother. "*Das ist logisch!* They would have begun to call it the Old Castle to contrast with the New Castle." They took in the view a moment longer. "I've never seen the mountains as clear as they are today!"

"*Nur für uns, nicht wahr?*" Theodor said.

"*Ja,*" agreed Adolf. "A farewell view, just for us,"

They turned their attention to the room's interior. "It looks like we are about to find out what *das Fräulein* wrote here." They approached a stand holding a composition book hand-written in German script. The page to which the book was open read, "*Das alte Schloß.*"[35] The brothers smiled at each other and said, "*Natürlich!*" It was not their first encounter with the poem, but now they looked to verify the items she mentioned. The first two verses:

Auf der Burg haus' ich am Berge, Housed am I in a mountain castle,
Unter mir der blaue See 'Neath me low the blue lake lies

"She's captured the spirit of her surroundings all right," Adolf said, before reading on.

Höre nächtlich Koboldzwerge	Nightly hear I goblins imp
Täglich Adler aus der Höh,	Daily eagles in the skies,

"*Gewiß!* As a child I always felt the place was so spooky when I came to deliver milk," Theodor said. "Dark halls, rough walls, unexplainable shadows, as if any moment a bogeyman might jump out at me."

Adolf laughed, then read the next two verses.

Und die grauen Ahnenbilder	And the gray ancestral portraits
Sind mir Stubenkameraden,	Room companions are for me,

They studied the likenesses of nobility on the walls. One was a bishop from Konstanz, another a prince from one of the vast number of principalities of the author's time.

Wappentruh und Eisenschilder	Weapons chest and iron shields
Sofa mir und Kleiderladen	Sofa mine and clothing tree.[36]

"There's the chest where she most likely stored her folded clothes, which also serves as a bench, and there are the shields where she hung her clothes."

Theodor would like to have read the rest of the five stanzas, but Adolf was too concerned about time. As they were leaving, the watchman approached. "Here, I have some picture postcards of the Old Castle for you to take to America and a few samples of the young lady's paper cuts."

"That, too? *Danke schön, Herr Wächter.*"

"A good beginning *dort drüben,*" he wished. "I'll press my thumbs for you."

"*Danke schön!* We'll arrive over there in about four weeks, five at most," Adolf said, as he preceded his brother across the bridge. He looked back. "Now we really have to hurry. We have just enough time to pick up the trunk and get those last-minute items for *Mutter.*"

He was already turning back to the *Steigstraße,* but Theodor had paused at the end of the bridge. How could his brother lose the mood so quickly? "*Ach, AH-dohlf,* she'll be thrilled that we saw the Old Castle. She'll not mind if we take one last look at *das Neue Schloß* either."

"*TAY-oh-door!*" Adolf scolded, but he grudgingly followed Theodor's footsteps in the other direction along the narrow, winding street with its abrupt, jagged turns. All the while, Adolf was muttering how their sister had come all the way from Ludwigshafen, how the womenfolk were washing their clothes for the trip and organizing the packing, and who knows what else? Then the narrow street opened up, and the pink stucco palace rose before their eyes. It was ornately trimmed with white flourishes in a flamboyant Baroque style.

In the 1700s the bishopric of Konstanz had decided it needed a delegation on the other side of Lake Constance to strengthen a growing but flagging congregation. However, the austere living conditions in the *Meersburg* repulsed the priesthood concerned. Finally, new quarters consistent with their current amenities made the offer more attractive. Thus resulted the New Castle.[37]

The boys had never been inside due to the fact that use of the residence was restricted to official visits and municipal functions. "This is a palace!" exclaimed Theodor the moment they entered. Could they possibly have a look around? They'd only be a minute. The guard on duty also recognized them as the ones who were emigrating from Germany and gave permission.

Inside the *Barockschloß* parquet floors so shiny the boys could see their reflections, voluptuous arcades, ample stairways, buxom statues, cherubic angels, and wrought-iron work all lent themselves to the bishops' idea of gracious living and entertaining. As they concluded their tour, the brothers were again loaded with appropriate postcards to take to America.

Finally, much to Adolf's relief, they were back on the *Steigstraße*, whose marked ascent had noticeably diminished, but whose width was still sufficiently cramped. The smell of coffee floated from a *Kaffeestube*, which was just getting back into business, and next door a bakery with its yeasty odors made them quicken their steps. At the *Marktplatz* they turned off to the *Meister's*. Theodor toyed with the idea of accepting an invitation for *Kaffeepause*, if received, then dismissed it, realizing this time it would be inappropriate.

Not long thereafter, the two were back at the *Marktplatz*, carrying the trunk by a handle at each end. The square afforded a good view of the *Restaurant zum Bär*, one of the town's most prominent restaurants.

Its cantilevered corner tower and its bay windows allowed views in almost all directions. Lately the windows sported geranium flower boxes as they had before the Great War. The town's merchants were probably enjoying coffee with *Schlagobers* and *Apfelkuchen*.

"This is another reason why we have to come back to Meersburg, to eat here, in the Restaurant to the Bear." Theodor murmured. They set the trunk down for a while. "I tell you what. Why don't you get those things for *die Mutter* while I stay with the trunk?"

"*Gewiß!*" Adolf said.

In Adolf's absence, Theodor thought suddenly of how he had never had an opportunity to snag a 10.000 Mark bill to keep as a souvenir. Of course, now that bill would be more appropriately 1.000.000 Marks. However, even a 100.000 Mark bill would be impressive.

Meersburger scenes: (above) Market Square with the Restaurant to the Bear in the foreground and the Upper Town Gate in the distance; (below from left) Lower Town with the Lower Town Gate in the distance; Old Castle (AD 628); the New Castle (1700s)

Adolf reappeared in a short time. They turned north from Market Square. Beyond loomed the *Oberstadttor*, its gabled, tower almost mirroring the *Dagobert Turm* of the Old Castle. They went through the Upper Town Gate and walked backward a ways, pondering what had once provided access to the city in medieval times. "Imprint this on your mind, Adolf."

"*Jawohl!* I think I saw this scene among the postcards they gave us."

The wall, circling the original town, had protected it from invaders by land. Many such towns, as settlements grew outside the enclosed center, tore down the wall and replaced it with a thoroughfare, usually called a *Ringstraße*.[38] But Meersburg had no "Ring Street." Its wall still stood. The stones were in good condition, and apartments had even been built on top of the wall. The construction therefore looked unusual, being blank until halfway up, where suddenly windows dotted the stone. Theodor was thinking ahead of how Americans would react when he received a letter from his friend Anton who lived in one of those apartments with the return address "On the Wall."

As they veered northwest on the *Daisendorfer Straße* on the final stretch, Theodor was reflecting how, often, when he was still an apprentice, he had walked this way on many a Sunday to visit the family in Daisendorf. He confessed to Adolf, "I'm going to be sorry to leave Meersburg. It has so much to offer . . . just think, two castles, two city gates, good restaurants, the lake promenade with its row of hotels, the ferry that stops at various ports around Lake Constance."

"*Ja*, shabby as it still is, what with the postwar conditions, it's still picturesque."

"*Ja*, and it will come back, it will come back. I'm thinking the New Country is going to be rather plain by comparison"

"*Ja, lieber Bruder*," said Adolf, "we have to take that into account. There will be no castles, no fortresses, no moats, no luxurious palaces, and—," he paused, "—probably no mill wheels."

"Then we'll have to come back. Yeah, we'll have to come back to the Old Country."

"*Ja, nach Meersburg am Bodensee.*"

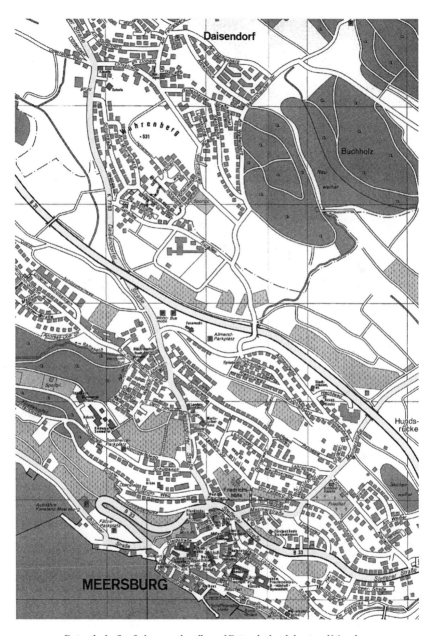

Daisendorfer Straße between the village of Daisendorf and the city of Meersburg

EPISODE SEVEN

DAISENDORFER GEMÜTLICHKEIT

Daisendorf

When the brothers arrived home, the mother greeted them with, "Where have you been? We've been waiting a long time."

The coffeepot was steaming. The house smelled strangely more fragrant than usual. Could it be real coffee? The hard rolls were on the table along with jam made from their plum tree. And was that butter? The girls nodded to their inquiring looks, meaning that they had churned it today. Cheeses, cold cuts, and pickles completed the offerings. Several serving platters also occupied the table mysteriously empty, as if waiting for more arrivals.

The family was already seated at the long plank table. Adolf gave Theodor an I-told-you-so look. But Theodor stiffened and confronted his mother. "*Ach, Mütterchen, du weißt . . .*" Adolf was thinking—here he goes again with an oh, dear Mama, you know . . . "We just wanted to take a look at the city, you know, one last time." Theodor finished.

Adolf was about to shoot him another look, this one speak-for-yourself, but thought better of it, when the mother merely answered, "*Ach ja, die Nostalgie.*" Theodor realized that his mother's question had stemmed not so much from anger as concern. Noticing that they were not carrying anything but the trunk, she asked, "You did get the herbal teas and the packets of glacé I asked for? And what about the 4711 cologne?[39] And Dr. Oetker's latest cookbook?"[40]

"*Ja*, we got everything you asked for. We put the trunk to use. The tickets are in there, too."

"*Ja!* The tickets," the mother said, as if the prime purpose of their errand had slipped her mind until now. Soon everybody was clamoring to see them.

"Oh-h," murmured Emilie happily. "Norddeutscher Lloyd Steamship Company."[41] Then her expression changed. "But they're steerage tickets. I thought you said those were risky to your health."

"*Ja*, but the tickets are on a freighter," explained Anna hastily. "That means there are no first- or second-class passengers, so they have the privilege of going on deck whenever they want."

"I see," clucked Emilie, "you got the best of both worlds!"

"*Natürlich!*" Marie declared. "The cheapest tickets with fresh air on deck."

Family members gingerly handled the tickets as they moved around the table. Different utterances emanated from the group. "They're going on the *Hannover*."[42] "They expect the trip to take four weeks." "From Bremerhaven." "Destination is New York." "*Ja*, Ellis Island."

The brothers took their places with the rest, and soon all were sinking their teeth into *Wasserbrötchen*, with their crusty outsides and their chewy insides. But Anni complained, "*Milchbrötchen sind doch besser.*" The three-year-old had a harder time chewing water rolls than milk rolls. She found those made with milk softer than those made with water. "*Leider*, these were what was left. *Aber wir haben Butter*," chanted Berta. "You helped us churn it, *weißt du?*"

"*Ach ja*," Anni said, mimicking her grandmother. "*Butter, bitte!*"

When Marie had a chance, she whispered to Emilie, "What do you think of Theodor's eye?"

"It appears healed, thanks to you, *meine Schwestern*," Emilie, sitting between Marie and Anna, whispered back. "I'll take a closer look later to see if he should stay on the medication."

"*Danke schön, Schwester Schwester*," the sisters said, mimicking Theodor's play on words about his sister nurse.

The women shooed them from the table unexpectedly soon. When next they looked the dirty dishes had disappeared. Cakes adorned the empty platters, an *Obsttorte*, its fruit covered with glaze, a poppy seed loaf cake, and other assorted baked goods, including a plum cake.

Not long after, from outdoors arose muffled noises that silenced the people inside. They strained to hear, at last catching the phrase: " . . . *Seid ihr bereit?*" Someone was asking, "Are you ready?" Soon they knew for what. A chorus broke out in folk song. "*Schön ist die Welt, drum Brüder, laßt uns reisen, wohl in die weite Welt, wohin es uns gefällt.*" The voice must have been from Barber Schnitzler, preparing to lead them in song.

When the singing went on after the first stanza, they expected it was the second. But no, it was a solo, and it was not in German. Finally they realized that it must be Teacher Lehrer, fitting an English translation into the notes. After all, he explained to them later, you better get used to English. "Fine is the world, therefore brothers let us travel, right into the wide world where'er it pleases us." That finished, Friedrich opened the door and in filed the inhabitants of Daisendorf.

"Finally someone from us is answering the call of the *Wanderlust*," boomed Innkeeper Wirth. Funny, Theodor mused to himself—*wandern, I* just mentioned "the travel bug" in the form of *Wanderbursche*, also called *Geselle*, the other day to Adolf. It seems a little odd, he had commented to Adolf, that instead of journeying around our own country, we're journeying to the New Country to practice our Old Country trades.

Next, Innkeeper Wirth handed the boys a large pouch. Inside was a variety of *Marks* and *Pfennige*. Apparently he had taken up a collection among the farm community. "Pocket money *für unterwegs*." Frau Innkeeper elaborated, "For on the way from Meersburg to Bremershaven."

The crowd spent some time savoring the cakes for which the mother had provided a bowlful of whipped cream. They relished the rare treat of real *Bohnenkaffee*, for Emilie was covering the cost of real bean coffee, enough for two whole pots for the celebration.

As they ate and joked, they examined details on the tickets, viewed the postcards, photos and gifts for the relatives in the New Country, and studied the map to trace the route they would take to the coast. Theodor confided to Adolf during the evening, "I'll bet it's a long time before we enjoy such *Gemütlichkeit.*"

But when they brought out the beer, Anna and Marie decided this was enough congeniality. "We can't be up all night. We've got work to do tomorrow." The neighbors reluctantly left.

Prime concern next day was taking care of the document box so that it was well protected. They inserted bottles of 4711 cologne and *Weißherbst* among the layers of soft items in the trunk. Photos and postcards needed to be packed away from glass, which might crack and spill its contents enroute. When Theodor and Adolf noticed some wine, they inquired almost in unison where it had come from. They were informed that the Meyers from the winery had come past the other day with two bottles of white autumn wine for them to take along.

"I hope they fit," said Marie.

"For local *Weißherbst* we'll make room."

"Our uncles will be delighted. They probably haven't had our *Weißherbst* since they left."

The final step in packing was to chink the gaps in the contents, using boxes of herbal tea and envelopes of cake glaze as well as socks and hankies so that nothing shifted position in transit.

As he was falling asleep that night Theodor was thinking— *Wunderbar!* Still, the missing 100.000 Mark bill popped into his mind. The people in America would not believe the bill would buy less than a pound of butter. But he quickly discarded the thought, knowing it was an imposition in Germany's present-day depression. When they reached the coast, perhaps they would have some bills leftover in the pouch that the Daisendorfers had given them. Even 5.000 Marks, the market price for one egg, would be nice.

The next morning, as they loaded the trunk on the wagon, the whole family was shedding tears. Finally Berta nudged her daughter toward Adolf. "*Gib ihm eine Umarmung!*" After Anni had hugged him, Berta said, "And now Theodor."

As Theodor bent down to the child's embrace, he spotted a piece of paper sticking out from her apron pocket. "Hey, you're losing something.

We don't want it to fall out." Anni looked at her mother hesitatingly.

"I should say not," said Berta.

Theodor pulled at it and out came a gray envelope of the coarse, cheap paper in common usage since the Great War. He was ready to hand it to Anni, when Marie said. "*Schau mal drin.*" Her eyes sparkled with mystery.

"*Ich? Was ist das?*" Theodor asked puzzled. He looked inside, as Marie had commanded, and jolted in surprise. "A couple of 100.000 Mark notes? But the villagers already gave us spending money."

"*Aber nicht unterwegs ausgeben,*" Anna cautioned.

"Not to spend on the way? *Aber, wofür denn?*"

"*Für euch!*" Marie exclaimed. "*In Amerika!*"

Theodor kept turning the bills over. "For us?"

"*Jawohl!*" the family shouted. As the idea sunk in, Theodor said, "*Um Gottes willen,* they're worth two whole pounds of butter!"

"For heaven's sake," they quipped. "We talked it over among us."

"Are you sure you can manage without it?" Their faces could not cover their disbelief.

"*Aber natürlich!*" Marie shrugged. "By tomorrow they will no longer buy even one pound of butter."

"But naturally," the rest chimed together. They laughed nervously at the utterance, all too conscious of its veracity.

"Besides, if we really want butter, as you have seen," reminded Anna, "we can make our own." The rest gave a gesture of unconcern, knowing in reality that was not the point.

"*Na schön, wir danken dafür.*"

"Don't thank us. It has no monetary value neither here or there, but when this is all over, you're right, you will want some rare souvenirs to look back on this crazy era," Marie said, even though in reality everybody knew that normalcy was still a long time coming.

With that, *die Mutter* suddenly drew her sons to her desperately, saying, "I know I'm never going to see you again." The boys tried to comfort her, yet they also knew the words of the mother, a widow already for thirteen years, could well be true.

EPISODE EIGHT

OLD COUNTRY TRAIN TRIP

"Do you have your money in a safe place?" the mother demanded, as they took their baggage outside. "When you take out your wallet, don't let everybody see all your money, or you'll wind up without any for the rest of the trip."

"*Ja, ja, Mutter,*" they answered. They took one last look at the house, where the initials of the three kings, K+ M + B, had been written with chalk blessed in church on the last sixth of January for the Feast of Epiphany. As they assembled their gear, the neighbors began emerging from their duties, congregating in the Daisendorfer commons. Friedrich had meantime brought up the wagon and horses. He was already sitting in the driver's seat. The trunk had been loaded. "Come on, Adolf and Theodor, get in so we can see how much room we have left," urged the others. In the end, the whole family fit in the wagon as well as a couple of neighbors. Those remaining behind shouted, "We'll press our thumbs for you!"

At the train station, Theodor's best friend, Anton, was waiting and his *Meister* and others they knew. With the help of Theodor's friend, Friedrich hoisted the trunk from the wagon and they loaded it onto the train. The three sisters handed them a satchel of food and drink to start them on their way. Besides the trunk, one traveler carried a shoulder bag to hold the bills and papers too bulky for their pockets, and the other a suitcase for everyday needs.

"*Macht's gut in Amerika,*" they wished, to which the boys replied, "*Versprochen!*"

The train went into motion. The two looked back to see the scene distancing itself. *Die Mutter* was waving her white handkerchief, and their sisters were huddled together. Berta had Heini in her arms, with little Anni clinging to her long skirt. Friedrich was still sitting on the driver's seat, ready to go back to the farm chores. Soon details blurred. Only a white, wavering spot remained among the drabness. Then the train slid over a hill and Daisendorf disappeared amid the grapevines.

Ambiguous feelings erupted within Theodor. Was it fear of the unknown in the New Country or nostalgia for the Old Country? *Um Gottes willen,* he thought—I'm feeling this way and we've hardly left Meersburg. From time to time he looked over at the sleeping Adolf. While the twenty-year-old youth caught up on sleep, the almost nineteen-year-old looked out the window.

After a short distance, the landscape was already changing. Theodor settled himself into position for the next few days with a book at his side about recent relationships between Europe and America for when he tired of looking. Adolf, too, enjoyed watching the countryside, but also spent some moments catching up on sleep from an overtime job he had wanted to complete before leaving.

As they proceeded northward, they challenged the countryside to confirm what they had learned in school. The country's topography should slowly descend as they made their way from the deeply cut Alpine foothills in the south to the flat coastal areas in the north. Indeed, the rough terrain soon relaxed into billowing hills, then the midlands vacillated between high and low mounds, which in turn softened into rolling hills. The landscape outside the window was constantly changing. Farm communities nestled in ridges. Now and then they could make out a cluster village like theirs or a street village, which followed the length of a valley, showing clearly its access to a market on the street at one end and to a stream at the other.

Around five days later, Theodor found the landscape suddenly disturbing. He shook his sleeping brother and called excitedly, "*Wach auf, Adolf!* We're arriving at the *Ruhrgebiet.*[43] Adolf, wake up!"

Finally Adolf jumped up and scrambled to the window. They were traveling through the eastern edge of the industrial Ruhr region. They had observed singular piles of rubble on their way northward, but they were not prepared for the present condition of the steel industry. Pictures in their schoolbooks, which showed chimneys emitting black smoke into the sky, never revealed a pretty sight. But the view in front of them was tragedy. The area was in parts completely leveled. Activity was minimal. Here and there a soldier in French or Belgian uniform roamed through the debris, but not a single steelworker was to be seen. Rubble had been pushed aside and piled high to allow space to walk. The sight simply denied the bustling photos they knew from their history books. Nothing relieved the dreariness, not even a flower, not even the sunny day.

The two tore themselves away from the window. But now nearby passengers' comments protruded upon their ears in sketchy phrases: " . . . protests of the steelworkers . . . demands of the French and Belgians . . . stakes too high . . . look at the inflation rate . . . Versailles Treaty demanded much more than the agreement had originally stipulated . . . ah, the Fourteen Points impossible to fulfill . . . of course, we're guilty, but . . . steelworkers on strike . . . " and a new expression for them "passive resistance. . . ."[44] They were glad to leave the depressed, depressing, dingy, dirty district, which brought home the worst of the present economic depression. The scene was as somber as a Käthe Kollwitz charcoal sketch. [45]

"How are we going to get out of this mess, Adolf, if we don't have the means to recover?"

"Ja, Theodor, except why do you say 'we'? Is it perhaps no longer our concern?"

Theodor was silent a moment. "You don't think we're avoiding difficulty by leaving?"

But Adolf let the question dissipate into the air.

Theodor thought—here I am, already failing to count only the sunny hours. But soon the landscape turned lively again and with it their mood. They were entering the third major topographical area that crossed their country in horizontal stripes like their flag, that of the coastal lowlands. They found themselves in the land of moors, heathered turf, and occasional windmills. As the train edged farther north, it looked as if a gigantic flatiron had exerted pressure on the topography until not even a wrinkle abided. Instead of the plentiful Alpine rose, blue gentian, and *Edelweiß* in their Alpine area, here close-cropped purple heather reigned, and now and then a sand dune broke the flushness of the coastlands, a far cry from their landscape at home, which made streets like the *Steigstraße* in Meersburg necessary.

Just after the *Ruhrgebiet* a different conductor boarded the train. Theodor was puzzled to find he couldn't understand him. Adolf was asleep when the conductor came past requesting something incomprehensible. Finally Theodor realized he needed to show their tickets again.

He watched the disappearing uniform, shaking his head. Change he had expected, but he had not expected to have a problem understanding the language before he left his home country. Maybe the conductor was not German. But that couldn't be. He wore a German railway uniform. They had to be talking the same language.[46]

Variations within a language group, he knew, were called dialects. In Meersburg he knew their Upper German dialect differed from standard or High German. Strangers came through every so often with a curious speech pattern, but usually one caught on shortly to the distinction.

The Steigstraße which connects the Lower and Upper Towns in Meersburg.

Dialects, according to Adolf, who had a brush with other pronunciation habits during his electrician's job in the zeppelin factory[47] in Friedrichshafen, were supposedly understandable among themselves. Then why couldn't he understand the conductor?

Not long after, they arrived in Bremen where the conductor announced an extended stop. The two emigrants had run low on food and headed immediately to the stands. The odor of bread, sausage, and mustard wafted toward them. "I'll go there, and you get some fruit," said Adolf. Theodor watched his brother head in the direction of the aroma. *"Brot mit Wurst und Senf, zweimal,"* he heard his brother say, modifying his Upper German dialect to his best High German.

Satisfied that he was not having trouble, Theodor proceeded to find a fruit stand. *"Zwei Äpfel,"* he ordered.

"Bitte?" the clerk asked.

"Zwei Äpfel," Theodor repeated. When the clerk still didn't understand, Theodor raised his voice, as if talking louder would make him more understandable. "EP-fel, EP-fel!" he boomed. The clerk shook his head. Theodor heard the clerk say something like *"Wat iss dat?"* with growing impatience. Theodor, now alert to the familiar phrase, realized he would have to point to the apples. The clerk clapped a hand to his head. "Oh, *appel*. Why didn't you say so? How many?" He held up different combinations of fingers.

Theodor, his frustration abating, held up thumb and index finger.

"Ja, two of them," the clerk said. *"Twee appel."*

"Twee appel, ja," Theodor mimicked the clerk's pronunciation as best he could, then said in his best High German, *"und ein Pfund Weintrauben,"* and pointed to the grapes as well.

"Ein pund," the clerk repeated. *"Jawohl! "* Then the clerk said something that sounded to Theodor like *Ik mok dat fertik.*

When Adolf saw his brother returning, fruit in hand and triumphant expression on his face, he said, "I see you made out all right."

"Gewiß!" They traded the extra portions of bread and fruit, then dipped the sausage into the mustard and felt its skin burst in their mouths. It was their first hot food since they had left Meersburg almost

a week ago. Finally Theodor was ready to talk. "When I said *Äpfel*, he said *appel*."

"*Richtig!* That sounds familiar. The fellows I worked with at the zeppelin factory, Klaas and Dirk, from the Hamburg area, that's the way they said it. *Ja, 'appel'* is lowland speech."

Theodor related the rest of his encounter, and added, "When he handed me the package, he said, '*Dat iss dat.*' That's that." Theodor laughed. "That reminded me of those nonsense syllables we kids used to recite. Remember? It went something like: '*Wat iss dat? Dat iss dat.*'"

Adolf finished the rhyme: "*Wenn iss nit, dann iss dat nat,*" then joined Theodor in laughter.

Back in the train, they settled in for the last stretch of some fifty kilometers to the port of Bremerhaven. "It sure feels good to eat something besides cheese and crackers," Adolf said, his eyelids already drooping. Theodor, too, was just about asleep when he saw the conductor approach again. Theodor shook his sleeping brother. "*Wach auf,* Adolf! Wake up, you have to help me again!"

"What?" Adolf raised his head sleepily. "*Was ist los?*"

"The conductor is going to want something and I might not understand." He did stop at their seats, and as he bent to hand them a tattered business card he had just withdrawn from his breast pocket, Theodor noticed that his name tag said "Loppnow." It appeared that Herr Loppnow wanted to convey something from the card to them. He showed them what looked like a British name, after which was the word "philologist," which he said meant *Philologe* in German. "That's someone who studies languages," he explained. Then the official turned the card over where the passenger had written something by hand.

The train official went on in Low German. Not every word was comprehensible to them, but with the aid of gesticulations and the fact that some words mimicked the German they spoke, they deduced his message. "I kept the card because every once in a while it's useful. The three sentences are all saying the same thing. The first sentence uses Standard or High German: *Ich mache das Wasser heiß.* The second is in Low German: *Ik mok dat Water heet.* And the last is in English: I'll make the water hot."[48] After mulling over the comparison a minute, they said, "*Ach ja! Wir verstehen!*"

When the conductor was about to depart, Theodor said, "*Moment mal.*" He gestured he wanted to copy down the three sentences. It gave the conductor a chance to say something else. "Do you know what the Englishman said after that?" The conductor's eyes displayed mirth. "He said that English and German are sisters!" He slapped his thigh. "*Ja, Schwestern!*" He left them chuckling.

Theodor turned to his brother. "Well, I don't know about sisters, but do you see how close English is to Low German in these sentences?" Theodor had written the three directly beneath each other.

"*Richtig!* Closer than either to Upper German."

"In that case, if we knew a little *Plattduütsch*,[49] it might help us learn English, Adolf!"

"Or as Klaas and Dirk told me, knowing the key to the corresponding sound in the other language helps to understand it," Adolf quoted.

"It makes me wonder how you say *appel* or *Apfel* in English."

Adolf didn't answer, but asked instead, "Do you realize it's only a month or so until we're in English-speaking territory?"

But Theodor was still wondering what Adolf's co-workers had meant by the key to corresponding sounds.

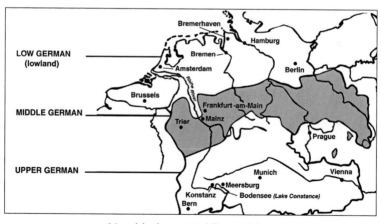

Map of the three principal German dialects

On board the ship Hannover

Back Row—far left–Adolf Ritsche, (Back row)—third from left–Theodor Ritsche

PART TWO

Across the Big Pond – Summer 1923

"If you want to be free, there is but one way; it is to guarantee an equally
full measure of liberty to your neighbors. There is no other."

— Carl Schurz, German-American statesman

POINT OF ORIGIN

Theodor and Adolf found their first view of the harbor at Bremerhaven breathtaking. Ships abounded, moving up and down along the Weser River. Even though the ships often obstructed a clear vision beyond, from the little Theodor and Adolf could glean between the spaces, they could imagine the channel spewing its contents into the North Sea. Every so often, mists of water sprayed over them, cooling the atmosphere. Rather than the odor of sausage and mustard typically wafting in the public areas that they were used to inland, here on the coast the odor of oily fish and acrid vinegar permeated the air.

The dock was strewn with cloth bundles tied with scarves or tattered rags, cardboard boxes held together with cord, worn leather cases, dented and mottled tins, feather beds, and pillows rolled tight with leather belts. Thin loaves of sausage and bread peeked from packages. Dolls and bears occupied children's arms, some so tightly squeezed that one would have thought the stuffing would burst through, others so loosely held that they dragged on the ground.

Some people were sitting on suitcases or trunks, freeing their hands for other pursuits. Parents or older children were reading to younger tots. Those in the *Flegeljahren*, children old enough to have achieved semi-independence, were playing dominos or marbles with each other, or running about the wharf. Some women were crocheting or embroidering or tatting lace, their toddlers patting the work, delighting at the different fabric textures. Someone was crooning to a fussing child.[50]

As Theodor and Adolf joined the people on the wharf, they heard a boy about four years old bawling, "I don't want to go on that boat." "Well, you have to," the parent cried. "We can't leave you behind." "No," the child screamed and stamped its feet. "I want to go back to *Köln*, back to *Oma's*." Suddenly, as if realizing that terror was prompting the child's outburst, the parent knelt down and looked intently into the child's eyes. "I know, *mein Liebling*, but that's out of the question. Grandma in Cologne can't take care of you. She's just not up to it."

At the parent's sudden tenderness, the child folded its arms around the bigger figure, who hugged it tight. "My darling, everything's going to be all right."

The girth of the ocean liners overwhelmed even the two brothers. The ships would dwarf the boats on the *Bodensee*. Imagine a child seeing such gigantic vessels for the first time. Wouldn't it be instilled with apprehension?

Near a barrier that kept the passengers from going closer to the waterway, they heard a child ask, "When are we going to see the musicians?"

"What musicians, *mein Schätzlein?*"

"The donkey and the pig and the cat and the rooster, and their instruments."

"Oh, the *Bremer Stadtmusikanten*. You're right, my little treasure. But the musicians are from Bremen. That was farther inland. Remember when the train passed through that crowded area some kilometers back?"

The youngster nodded.

"That was the city of Bremen. But now we're in what's called Bremen Harbor."

The child thought a moment. "So we won't see them?"

"I'm afraid not, *Schätzlein*." The mother looked down at the innocent face. "You liked that story so much?"

"*Ja*." The tot's eyes turned wistful.

"What part did you like so much?"

"The part when they all climb upon each others' backs."

The mother giggled. "*Siehst du, mein Kind?*" then repeated, "Do you see, my child? You still have the story with you."

With peels of laughter in their ears, the two brothers moved into the crowd. They noted groups of girls in gaudy bandannas, bands of boys in brimmed caps, men in what was probably their only suit, and women in long, ample skirts, that appeared much too hot even in the cooler weather of the north. But the emigrant brothers were told those skirts had another function—they hid an enormous amount of baggage. It was easier to carry extra clothing on their backs rather than in their suitcases.

Signs of wear shone in some people. Their clothes were wrinkled, their dispositions cranky. Some were as unkempt as *Struwwelpeter*.[51] The brothers wondered how long they had been waiting. Theodor was ready to put down their trunk, too, but Adolf countered, "First we must have our tickets validated, remember?"

"*Ach ja, richtig!*"

They asked around if anyone knew where the freighter *Hannover* docked. Someone pointed the way to the confirmation booth. The brothers headed in that direction lugging their trunk, which seemed to weigh more as time went on.

At the booth they were in for a surprise. Between purchase and embarcation dates, inflation had risen so much that the brothers had to pay an additional amount. The unexpected surcharge left a huge dent in their spending money. As they left, Theodor said, "Unfortunately, that didn't take away my appetite."

Adolf said, "*Du hast Hunger?* And now I suppose we shouldn't spend the money."

"*Ja*, I'm hungry." Theodore shrugged. "But I was thinking, we'll be on the ship soon."

But Adolf rebutted, "*Nein*, we still have a long wait. *Ich habe auch Hunger!* But won't we need to keep some aside for on the ship?"

"*Im Gegenteil*," said the younger brother. "Remember! There's nothing to buy because the food is included."

"*Gut*," concluded the older brother. "*Dann essen wir!*"

It was decided, while Theodor guarded the trunk, Adolf would find them something to eat. "I think all you have to do is follow your nose." They had already passed gigantic barrels filled with herring languishing in a pickled sauce with sliced onions and whole peppercorns at a stand bearing the brand name *Nordsee*.

"*Ja*, I'm anxious to compare the taste of fish from the sea with our lake fish."

In Adolf's absence, Theodor watched the slowly moving throng. The dock was at the moment so crowded, people had to move slowly so as not to cause an upheaval to baskets or babies. In the process he caught more snatches of conversation.

"Why does the sign say 'HB', Mother?" a little boy was asking. "Does it mean Harbor Bremen?"

Theodor saw the mother repress a laugh. "No, *mein Schatz*, it stands for for *Hansastadt* Bremen. The city once belonged to the Hanseatic League."[52]

"What was that?" the boy asked, as he walked along, kicking cheerily at stones in his path.

"Well, my dear, that was a trade union among states bordering on the North and East Seas from England to Russia way back in the fourteenth and fifteenth centuries. Holland, Germany and Sweden also belonged to it."

"Oh, so they had ships like these that went from city to city along the coast?"

"*Korrekt!* And you know what their most important cargo was?"

When the tyke paused, she said, "*Denk mal!* What would be most logical? Think!"

"Oh, I know, I know!" The chap's chest expanded. "*Fische!*"

"*Natürlich!* Fish like herring and cod. But, of course, other things were also traded—furs and amber, woods and grains from the east were exchanged for cloth and minerals from the west. Today Bremen and Hamburg are city states, *siehst du?* And they along with Lübeck are honored as having been members of the League by putting an H for 'Hansa' before their names. *Siehst du?*"

"Yes, now, I see," replied the boy. "The 'H' stands for 'Hansa', and . . . "

As their conversation faded, Adolf reappeared. When Theodor saw the pickled herring and fried cod, he exclaimed, "*Gut!* I was just listening to a mother telling her child about those exact items."

On the plates were also potato salad and bread, apples and oranges. "Remember what the person at the courthouse back in Meersburg said about oranges?"

Theodor nodded his approval. "*Ja,* we don't want to get scurvy. If only our *Schwester* Emilie could see you now."

They sat on their trunk devouring the food. The crowd thinned for a moment so that they could see a nearby group of some dozen people. They were obviously together, for the children were all wearing the same type coat and sailor hat. They were lined up in stairstep fashion from the biggest to the smallest, while someone was snapping pictures of them. Among the group were two adults, both men—Why weren't any mothers around? The boys wondered and suddenly paled as they realized the worst.—What an awful way to start a new life in America!

"We're not so badly off then, are we?" Theodor said to Adolf.

"*Ja,* all the responsibility we have is baggage."

"Especially the box!" Theodor reminded.—That's why he guarded the trunk so carefully, because of the box inside, thought Adolf.

The crowd suddenly became more pressing. They realized that embarkation time for an ocean liner had come and they were right in the path of the crowd funneling toward the ship. Not all were passengers they discovered, as only some mounted the gangplank. Many were farewell-givers who stepped back so they could wave to their party when it arrived on deck. There were few joyous good-byes, as if they realized it was their last. When the boat set itself in motion, those remaining behind left the dock. The view cleared but only for a moment. No sooner were the well-wishers gone than another train emitted its load onto the wharf.

After a while, Theodor said to Adolf, "Since our boat doesn't leave for several hours, do you mind if I walk around the deck a bit?" Adolf assured him he'd watch the trunk, because of the box inside.

It is good to stretch out—Theodor thought, as his legs welcomed the exercise. He couldn't remember when he had spent so much time sitting, first on the train and now on the wharf. Even when he worked at his bench, though much of the time was spent standing, he swayed and stepped in place a lot as he maneuvered saw, hammer, and chisel.

Theodor started talking with a man on the wharf. "Are you maybe from the Ruhr area?"

"Yes," said the man, and extended his hand. "The name's Kohler."

Theodor's question was merely to start a conversation. Though the man had on a suit, his grimy fingers and gritty fingernails betrayed his occupation as a coal miner. "Things are pretty bad there all right," Theodor said. "We traveled one edge of the Ruhr on the train here and it looked pretty grim. We had heard in the south where we're from that it was bad, but we were not prepared for so much devastation."

"Well, yeah, and on top of that there's no activity," the man replied. "The government was paying us for not working. Well, I don't know how long that's going to last when nothing is being produced. When I heard that, I thought, that's it, because eventually that's going to catch up with us."

"*Richtig!* Yes, and also because there's no gold backing. I think we must have given all our gold away by now."[53]

"The situation is terrible, there's no doubt about it."

Theodor made a circular motion to include the children running around. "So all these are yours?"

"Sure are. I'm going to Pittsburgh in Pennsylvania. Hoping to get a job in the steel mills."

"I hope you don't have a job yet." Theodor had heard that despite the fact that one went to America to work, it was also suspect if one had a prearranged job. Immigrants were not to take jobs from citizens. Theodor was relieved when the man said, "No, but my hands will show I'm experienced! *Nicht wahr?*" Theodor was about to voice agreement, but was spared by the appearance of the man's wife with another child in tow. "*Familie Kohler, kommt!* I have found something for us to eat."

"*Viel Glück, Herr Kohler!*" Theodor wished him.

"*Danke.* We need lots of luck," the man called as they retreated.

Theodor said, "*Auf Wiedersehen!*" since he had learned they would be on the same boat. Theodor looked around and saw a man who, judging by his clothes, must have slept in them. He was leaning against a trunk, a child on one arm and several little ones crouched around his feet, sleeping. The man suddenly yawned and opened his eyes a moment. The children kept on sleeping, except for one who was playing with a ball. He kicked it out of range and it headed toward Theodor, who promptly kicked it back.

The process made enough noise to alert the father..

Finally Theodor ventured, "It looks like you have been here for some time."

"Our second night on the wharf."

"Oh." Theodor was alarmed. "I hope they don't detain our boat. It's supposed to leave at seven tonight."

"Really? Ours, too." Theodor learned they were also going on the *Hannover*.

The man introduced his family as the Osterlands. They were coming from a German-speaking settlement in Romania. When Theodor expressed surprise, he told him about other German-speaking people coming from the east, from Yugoslavia and Czechoslovakia, from Hungary, Poland, and even the Ukraine. Often they were descendants of German colonists who had been invited in earlier times to improve the land, but now their progeny were no longer welcome. His family had been on the road now over two weeks. Most refugees went directly north to the coast, but the Osterlands had business with relatives in *Donaueschingen,* the source of the Danube, where his ancestors had come from originally.

"Oh," remarked Theodor. "*Im Schwabenland!* Very close to where I'm from." When the man nodded, Theodor asked, "So all these are yours?"

"*Ja*, these five and two more. My wife is someplace with my oldest tending the baby. Our oldest is fifteen. He's a big help to the family."

"So you have seven in all." Theodor paused. Eyeing him with all those little ones encircling about gave Theodor a warm, homey, feeling. "That's a nice size family," he said at last.

A young boy, carrying a placard which said "*Hannover,*" was milling through the crowd. He announced from time to time, "All passengers going on the *Hannover*, follow me."

"That's our ship. I better get back to my brother and the trunk," Theodor said. "*Richtig!* See you on board," Herr Osterland said.

Theodor thought—how nice that I've already met some of our fellow passengers. When he rejoined his brother, he said, "You know what? I found a German-speaking guy who's not even from Germany. He's from Romania, near the mouth of the Danube."

Finally, it was time to ready their tickets. Passengers shuffled slowly toward the gangplank. There were babies who had to be carried, the elderly, who could no longer walk, well supported by companions, overlarge suitcases including their trunk, all which encumbered forward movement.

The boarding process was slow, but finally the gangplank widened onto the boat. Children sped ahead of them, and when they reached the deck, they jumped up and down with glee, then rushed to the other side of the ship, whose height afforded a greater view of the aquatic expanse. Before the voyagers had even begun to put their things away, the freighter had started moving. Soon it was good-bye to the Old Country, no longer able to support its population, and onward to a New Country, with its promises and possibilities. Theodor and Adolf watched pensively as their land since birth faded into the dusk, then turned their attention in the other direction.

As they sailed into the North Sea, the smell of fish gradually dissipated. Even in the twilight they could see much more water than they had ever pictured. They had thought their so-called inland "Swabian Sea" was huge, but the North Sea far outranked the Bodensee. There would be nothing comparable to the Swiss Alps in the distance. There would be nothing at all. And beyond would beckon the Big Pond.

DOWN IN STEERAGE

The passengers soon found that conditions on board were as crowded as those on the wharf. Theodor left Adolf on deck with the trunk, while he descended the ladder with other passengers to see what steerage had to offer. Theodor wondered, slight as he was, if he would be able to stand up straight, because ceilings reportedly fell considerably short of two meters. To his amazement, he could stretch up to his full height. He heard others murmuring their approval.

"Ceiling height must have increased in recent times," Theodor observed aloud.

"Or freighters always had more allowance," commented a fellow traveler. He smiled as Theodor turned to him, holding out his hand to be shaken. "*Ich bin Walter.* Well, actually my full name is Johann Verwalter, but everybody calls me Walter."

"*Schon gut,*" Theodor said after he had introduced himself, then returned to his subject. "I don't know about floor space. We might have to work out sleeping room, if all of us passengers want to lie down at once." The few bunks were obviously not going to suffice.

"I think it's going to be okay, because there's another sleeping area. At any rate, the space allowance is better than the previous half-meter allowed the first time I crossed twenty years ago."

Theodor replied, "*Ja,* in that space, you can't even turn over comfortably.[54] So, this is not your first trip?"

"No, I just accompanied my aged aunt back to her hometown in

Germany to live out her days. She had come to visit my dad with the idea she might stay. But at her age it's hard to make a satisfactory adjustment, even in America. She missed the old, familiar ways. In her short time here, she had deteriorated so much that someone had to be with her on the cruise back."

Theodor nodded, then indicated the floor. "Now I see why so many carried *Federbetten*."

"Those down quilts certainly make the hard wooden floor easier to take, that's for sure."

"But the rumor—that we will not be confined down here below to steerage—turning out to be true, that's the best news," Theodor said. As he left Walter to explore more of the lower quarters, he was thinking—not to be shut off from view, rather to be able to look up to sky, sun, and stars, to see ocean and horizon, the sights would make the confined space more tolerable.

But Theodor was even more pleased when he came upon storage lockers in an enclosure beyond their sleeping area. Eagerly he went back up to tell Adolf of his findings, then hurried to find a crew member for a key. His feelings were soaring. He would no longer have to worry about his most prized possession, the symbol for achieving journeyman status in Europe. In America his certificate as *Geselle* would probably not matter. Nonetheless, presenting the box was sure to help him get a job.

The brothers had trouble negotiating the trunk down the rungs of the ladder. The opening to the lower level was narrow, allowing little head room. Finally they reached the bottom, and Theodor said, "*Schau mal, Bruder*, the compartment is big enough to store our trunk." Before stowing it inside, they raised its lid to check the status of the contents. The top layer revealed no evidence of spilled liquid or broken glass, so they decided not to chance digging down any farther.

When Theodor at last turned the key to the locker he heaved a sigh. "Things are looking up, *nicht wahr?*" He noted that Adolf, however, did not have the same apprehension about security. But then, he didn't have the same investment in the contents either. In addition to the box, which would forever distinguish Theodor as an Old Country woodworker, he also had his hammer. How clearly that scene with his *Meister* returned whenever he remembered his master teacher's gesture of benevolence. Theodor would never be able to use the tool without thinking how he had mastered driving a nail straight under his tutelage.

A few days later, the brothers felt the down side of the open sea. Not only had the seagulls disappeared, but a storm arose, whipping the ship up and down so violently that many were left seasick, including Adolf who remained prone below deck for several days. That the storm didn't let up immediately didn't help recovery. Adolf finally appreciated the *Underberg*[55] tonic for stomach ailments that their sister Emilie had tucked among cloth items in their suitcase. The bitters calmed his spasms a great deal.

Theodor began commenting about the eternal ups and downs, for it seemed to him that in the next few days, he was always going down the ladder, not only to monitor Adolf with the calmative, but also to nurse him with broth and water, and up the ladder with the pails of collected waste.

Finally a few days later, Adolf showed Theodor that he was not to be outdone by such repetitions when he retorted, "Well, it should be easy. You have had enough practice going up and down the 'Climbing Street' in Meersburg."

"*Stimmt's*," Theodor replied, thinking to himself—some thanks I get.

A passing officer who, though they were but a few days on their journey, had already noticed Adolf's absence on deck, advised Theodor, "When your brother gets back to eating regularly, have the galley prepare him some herring. The cooks say it works wonders for seasickness." Theodor turned away quickly to mask the thought that the suggestion would really not go over well with Adolf, since he had not been impressed with the pickled fish in Bremerhaven.

The passengers came to know the attendant as the Herr Offizier Niederung, a sailor who claimed the port city they had just left as his home. The travelers were soon to learn he would provide special privileges whenever he could devise a way.

Meanwhile, Theodor entertained himself getting acquainted with his fellow passengers, promptly passing information on to Adolf. His brother had met Walter during a time below. But now Theodor said, "There's an Englander aboard. His name's Charles Saxon. He keeps close to Walter. His German is pretty good, but when someone speaks in dialect, or too fast or on an unfamiliar topic, then he gets help from Walter." It was rumored that Charles had been on business in Germany when the American trip came up for him. He telegraphed his company in London that he opted to embark on a German ship rather than return first to an English port.

Jakob Friedman was also an atypical traveler from the majority on the ship. A well-dressed young man for boat conditions, he was forever reading something from either Goethe or Schiller, considered Germany's two greatest writers. His luggage must have contained mainly books, Theodor told Adolf, because whenever he saw Jakob, he had a different tome.

The voyagers for the most part complained the port smell had disappeared only to be exchanged for another foul odor. So they abandoned the "sick bay," taking their feather beds up on deck to spend the night under the starry skies, except, of course, when it rained. Then chanting could be heard from the secondary sleeping quarters: "*Es regnet, es regnet, es regnet seinen Lauf, Und wenn es hat genug geregnet, hört es wieder auf.*"

"*Ja,*" joked Theodor to Adolf, "so true, the rain will run its course, and when it's rained enough, it will stop. I guess that's also true of your stomach trouble."

But two young gentlemen had tolerated going down below. Stefan Lang, a tall, lanky lad who did indeed have a problem standing upright in steerage, had a shock of medium brown hair that stuck out from his brimmed cap. He had to double over to get down the steps to steerage. Theodor noticed him right away, since he walked around with a map of Europe in his shirt pocket, so he could locate people's origins. "Look here!" Stefan told Adolf when he was able to sit up a bit, "I put a dot on the map at Meersburg with your names next to it."

Then Adolf saw that Stefan's name was next to the city of Erlangen. "So that must be your home town," Adolf said.

Theodor learned that Michael Baumgartner, who also risked going below, was from Ulm and was going to New Ulm in Minnesota. "There's a good chance we might see more of each other in America," he said when he was introduced to Adolf below.

The story Adolf enjoyed most, however, was about the bright-eyed little boy Theodor had found wandering around one day on deck by himself. Theodor soon recognized him as the boy on the wharf who was learning about the letter "H" denoting "Hanseatic cities." The boy, now dressed in a smart-looking sailor suit with short pants and knee socks, was examining each protuberance and cavity with brisk, swift movements over the ship's exterior with one hand and a Teddy Bear in the other. After watching him a bit, Theodor asked, "*Wie heißt du, Kindlein?*"

The boy reacted immediately, giving Theodor an endearing smile. "*Ich heiße Hans.*"

"*Ach so*, and Hans, are you happy to be going into the wide, wide world alone?"

"I'm not alone." His chest swelled. "*Mutti und Vati sind dabei.*"

"Yes, Mom and Dad, but you are all going into the wide, wide world, *nicht wahr?*"

Before Hans could answer, his questioner began singing the children's song: "*Hänschen klein, ging allein, in die weite Welt hinein,*
        Stock und Hut, steht ihm gut, ist ja wohl Gemüt."

A gurgle proceeded from deep down inside the youngster as he caught the reference to the ditty. "Well, you obviously are full of good humor, but where's your cane and your hat?" Theodor asked.

"*Mein Stock? Mein Hut?*" Giving Theodor a demure look, he said slyly, "They don't fit me well." Theodor started at his quick allusion to the song, thinking—I'd like to see him after a year in the New Country.

Just then a couple appeared, looking for their *Hänschen*. When the pair noticed their son in conversation with Theodor, they commiserated about keeping others busy answering his questions.

"*Im Gegenteil,*" Theodor contradicted, holding out his hand to shake. They introduced themselves as the Grundigs. Finally Herr Grundig addressed his son. "We've been looking all over for you."

"I've been right here all the time," the boy said, looking at Theodor for confirmation. But Frau Grundig brushed aside the declaration saying, "*Aber komm' jetzt.* The captain has something to show you." The boy's eyes widened. "*Der Kapitän?* That's why you were looking for me?" Hans, anxious to know his surprise, skipped alongside his parents as they left the scene to make their way to the captain's quarters.

"*Vergiß nicht dein Bärchen!*" Theodor called after them, since the bear had been left, peeking from behind a pipe. Theodor noticed that it had a "*Knopf-im-Ohr.*" Button-eared bears meant it was from the Steiff company, which made plusher toys—and costlier—than other toy firms.[56]

EPISODE ELEVEN

UP ON DECK

Finally Adolf's stomach could bear more substantial food. Theodor had spent a day or two going up and down with thin oatmeal and soup. At last the recovered brother felt ready to join the others up on deck. The weather was heavenly! The sun was out, the waves serene, the ship as still as at dock, as if the turmoil had never happened.

After Theodor had brought breakfast to his brother, he said, "So, you're feeling well enough that you're finally going up on deck and getting to know better all the people I told you about." But he hadn't counted on the other person down under in steerage with a worse case of seasickness than Adolf's. In fact, most of the time Theodor had waited on him along with his brother. Now the man was not going to let Adolf go up on deck without him, even though he had not fully recovered like his fellow patient.

The Hannover

An assemblage of people who had come to congregate for meals at the same table, which they had come to call their *Stammtisch*,[57] was waiting for them—Michael and Stefan, Walter and Charles, the Grundig family, and Jakob, who had a book squeezed underarm. A portion of the cover showed the letters "Johann von . . . "—Aha, thought Theodor, another Goethe book.

Two couples, who seemed direct opposites from each other, had also joined their table. The first, the Seligmanns, seemed rather serious and nervous at first. In fact, Frau Seligmann had displayed a discomfort that seemed to get worse by the day. Finally she took a deep breath and, looking around at the group, said, "You know, it's been such a long time since we've done the mealtime blessing, not since we left home, *nicht wahr*, Matthias?" She looked at her husband next to her, then back at the group. "I miss that. We've always said prayers at regular times."

"Why, yes, Elisabeth!"

Michael Baumgartner, much relieved that the problem was now not only in the open, but also easily solvable, had affirmed, "I'm thinking we're going to miss our customs. Nevertheless, the adjustment will probably be easier on us young people, who haven't established our habits yet. So I say let the Seligmanns carry out their tradition." Frau Seligmann nodded to her husband, and soon the group became accustomed to him leading in prayer before each meal. When he finished, Frau Seligmann would lead the others, responding "Amen."

The Bayers, on the other hand, seemed a jovial couple from the beginning. They had greeted them on the first day with a *Grüß Gott*, giving away immediately that they were either from Bavaria or Austria. Now they wanted to welcome the newcomers into the group. "*Grüß Gott, Adolf! Grüß Gott*, Herr Kraenke!"

Theodor had been looking forward to the two patients rejoining the group. Instead the conversation took a different turn.

Herr Kraenke stared when he heard the greeting, probably seldom heard in his part of the country. "So where are you from?" he grunted. Flustered, Frau Bayer murmured, "Augsburg, where the Fuggers came from."

Also flustered at Herr Kranke's reaction, Herr Bayer sought to impress him. "*Ja*, home of the Fuggerei."

"Whatever that is," said Herr Kraenke.

Hoping that an explanation of others' generosity would mollify the man's humor, Herr Bayer could not resist pride in his voice. "Why, Herr Kraenke, that was probably the first large act of philanthropy the world has ever seen. It occurred already in the seventeen hundreds as a project of the Fugger family."[58]

"*Jawohl!*" added Frau Bayer, "a poor family could get a home for a '*Pfefferkorn*.'"

"For a what?" demanded Herr Kraenke.

"A peppercorn. You know, Herr Kraenke, for little or nothing," explained Stefan.

"*Ja*, cheap," added Michael.

But the look on Herr Kraenke's face continued to declare his dissatisfaction. The attempt to turn his gloom into gladness seemed futile. Herr Bayer made one last try to be conciliatory. "Our hometown will be two thousand years old by the end of this century."

Walter sought to keep up the change in subject. "*Wirklich?* And to think we're going to a country that isn't even two hundred years old. What do you think the lack of history and tradition is going to be like in America?"

"Our relatives, when they arrived in Minnesota about twenty years ago, said it was open land," Theodor said, trying to keep the momentum going, but to no avail.

Walter took a final shot at his lack of cheer. "Herr Kraenke, how would you like eating in a stifling bunk that has never been cleaned since it was built?" Herr Kraenke merely grunted and came out with other complaints. Walter intensified his threats, until he came to what he thought was the worst. "How would you like to find worms in your food?" The grumbler shifted his position a bit. "Herr Kraenke, think! That's what your ancestors went through when they came over. And now they're sponsoring you."

"*Ja!*" Now the Seligmanns chimed in soothingly. "Be grateful, Herr Kraenke."

Theodor had concluded that Herr Kraenke was an ungrateful person. Nonetheless, he was not prepared for his next comment. Herr Kraenke muttered, "If I had known that we would have such bad storms, I wouldn't have come."

His statement shocked the bystanders. Walter finally offered, "Come now, Herr Kraenke, this is nothing compared to what our forefathers experienced as emigrants." Charles Saxon, not keeping up with the rapid conversation and perplexed by odd gesticulations and colloquial expressions, stood close at Walter's side. Walter's occasional whispering brought nods to Charles' head, as Herr Kraenke persisted. "Hardly a week is up, and already we've had one bout of this. Who knows when the next will happen?"

Theodor lamented, "and we even shared our *Underberg* with him, he was so sick."

Moreover, the despair clearly offended the Seligmanns. "*O, es tut mir leid*, Herr Kraenke. My husband and I will pray that you feel better, *nicht wahr*, Matthias?"

"*Natürlich, meine liebe Elisabeth!*"

They knew they had failed to humor him, but they were interrupted by a strange phenomenon. Foam from behind a corner was curiously creeping toward them. The Bayers sped to see its source. As they peeked around the corner, they broke out laughing. When the rest caught up with them, they saw that passengers were taking advantage of the rainwater that the crew had collected the day before to get cleaned up. The fair weather meant fewer duties for the crew, so they were free to hoist the used water. A trail of suds in the ocean streamed out behind the ship. But apparently not all of the dirty water had made it overboard—some had spilled onto the deck to form rivulets in their direction.[59]

The passengers had strung up sheets to have separate compartments for men and women. The Herr Offizier Niederung passed by now and then to ask if he could get them anything.

Stefan, conscious of his oil-streaked hair, said finally, "Maybe we should join them."

"*Richtig!*" A bystander, out in the sun again, was toweling her hair as if to get out the last remnants of moisture. "The weather's fine, and you might not get a chance to bathe again before the trip ends." They learned she was Frau Kummer. Even though it was their first encounter with her, she gave them the impression that she hovered over people like a mother hen watching over her brood. "*Jawohl!* We can't have the immigration officials in America finding lice among us or, heaven forbid, some skin disease."

The men made their way past the sheets to their section. There they found Hans and his father already half-clothed. So that's why the Grundigs were not with the others. They watched Hans a minute, busily bursting bubbles.

Theodor Ritsche in a sailor's uniform aboard the Hannover

Freshly scrubbed, the young men joined the rest gathered in a group to dry their hair in the sun. The talk centered on postwar conditions, inflation, peace treaty requirements, and whether these circumstances were not complicating rather than ameliorating European affairs. The younger boys had already taken to their marbles or dominos. Soon the sheets were taken down, and across the way they could see women in their usual activities crocheting, embroidering, and reading or singing to their offspring. But a most surprising observation was suddenly voiced by Hans, when he claimed that the sour stench of illness had disappeared. Frau Kummer cut short their amazement when she got up to leave, saying, "Now, don't stay in the sun too long and get burned."

At last they gathered at their *Stammtisch* for supper. Herr Seligmann recited the customary prayer: "*Segne, Gott, diese Speise, Uns zur Kraft und Dir zum Preise.*" But this time no sooner had Frau Seligmann led the others in response than Herr Kraenke followed in his previous vein— whether the meal was really nourishing, if porridge and stews could really make them strong and were the provisions really worthy of praising God?

Frau Kummer, who joined their group for the first time, said resignedly, "*Um Gottes willen*, Herr Kraenke. We have to make the best of what we have. After all we're . . . " But the rest of the statement remained unspoken, for Herr Seligmann was shaking his head and Frau Seligmann broke in. "*Ja.* We mustn't be ungrateful." The rest couldn't tell whether her interruption was intentional or not.

But they had not long to ponder, for suddenly Jakob Friedman's face brightened. "As a matter of fact, I'd like to add a couple of verses from a poem I've been memorizing. You know Germany's greatest poet?"

"*Natürlich!* Johann Wolfgang von Goethe, everybody knows that." The crowd tried hard not to react to Herr Kraenke's haughty tone.

Jakob continued in an unperturbed manner. "In my hometown of Frankfurt, we honor Goethe because it's his birthplace." Theodor thought—maybe that's why Jakob focused his reading on the famous writer. "*Na schön.* A few verses come to mind that may be particularly appropriate right now. Would you like to hear them?"

"Oh, yes, do recite," the crowd found itself murmuring, a little astounded at its own bid for patience. Though poetry recitation was popular at home, there they would probably never have taken the time to listen.

"It's from a piece called '*Gesang der Geister über den Wassern*'," stated Jakob.

"*Des Menschen Seele gleicht dem Wasser:*
Vom Himmel kommt es, zum Himmel steigt es,
Und wieder nieder Zur Erde muß es, Ewig wechselnd."[60]

Walter was leaning toward Charles Saxon, the man from England, who by now was known by the German version of his name, Karl Sachsen. Way back, he conceded, his ancestors must have come from Saxony in eastern Germany, for the ancient Saxon tribe was common to both countries.

Now Walter said to Karl, "It's called 'Song of the Spirits over the Waters,' and in English goes something like this:

Man's soul is like water,
Proceeding from heaven and there returning
Eternal recurrence, to Earth yearning."[61]

The crowd remained hushed for a moment. Even Herr Kraenke dared not break the silence. They pondered the eternal cycle, up and down, up and down, but not in a vertical line, rather something more like a circle, and perhaps not a perfect circle, but more of an ellipse, but whatever its shape, at least unbroken. Gradually they left the table singly and went up on deck, each imagining the ocean evaporating into the sky only to return at a later time as drops of rain. Then they watched the sun until it set on the horizon toward which they were heading.

MAP MOSAIC

"Stefan," Theodor called out to his lanky friend passing by. "Let's see how your map is doing." The map of Europe was helping the guests place people, whose acquaintanceship was widening by the day. Adolf was finding the map an easy way to get caught up on people's names.

Their friend's medium brown eyes gleamed as he took from the pocket of his shirt, now soiled from many days' wear, his map and proudly showed it. "*Was meinst du?*"

"What do I think?" At a glance Theodor saw many more marks than on his last look. "*Erstaunlich!* You've really been around since I last saw the map."

The names belonged mostly to people they had already met. The Grundigs were there at Tübingen, a university town, Jakob Friedman had a dot on Frankfurt, the Bayers at Augsburg and, of course, Michael at Ulm and Stefan himself at Erlangen, the Seligmanns from a village on the Rhine. Frau Kummer was from a tiny village called Eschweiler, near Aachen, the former capital of the founder of the Holy Roman Empire, *Karl des Großen*,[62] and Herr Kraenke from Willstedt, near Bremen. Even the Herr Offizier Niederung merited a dot in Bremenhaven. Stefan Lang gave Karl Sachsen two dots on the map, one at London and the other at Leipzig, a prominent Saxon city. The Osterlands, who had gravitated to the crowd with families, were there at the mouth of the Danube. But there were others whose names Theodor didn't recognize. I still have people to meet, he thought.

Just then Michael Baumgartner joined them. Adolf took the opportunity to show his knowledge by pointing to a city a little northeast of Meersburg, "And you're from that city, Ulm." Michael turned to Theodor.

"Aha! You've been talking about me behind my back."

"*Das ist ja Unsinn!*" Theodor shot back, laughing.

"Oh, I know how much nonsense you talk," Michael rejoined.

But Theodor was looking closely at the map. "*Adolf, du hast recht.* On the map Ulm seems relatively close to Meersburg."

"At last, you're admitting I'm right," Adolf exulted.

Walter approached asking, "Where's my dot?"

"Right here at Koblenz,[63] where two tributaries flow into the Rhine, right here." said Stefan.

"*Genau!*" Herr Seligmann had suddenly appeared. "We come from that area, too, a little town no one's ever heard of."

Herr Bayer approached, with his wife not far behind. He called back, "Hey, Matilde, are we on the map?" She came running. "*Ich denke nicht,* Peter."

"*Grüß Gott,* everybody!" he said. "Just what we were asking about." Onlookers still couldn't suppress a smile at the southern greeting. "But you're already on the map," Stefan exclaimed. "*Augsburg, nicht wahr?*"

Herr Bayer answered, "*Jawohl!* You remembered where we're from!"

That wasn't hard, thought Stefan. Soon the map was drawing more passengers, ones they did not yet know by name. Bedlam ensued, because all wanted to approach at once.

"Hey, wait a minute," Theodor finally cautioned, "Let's not wrinkle the map." When the crowd had stepped back, he said, "Stefan, you'd be willing to put them on the map, wouldn't you?" The lad nodded. "I see he's got his pen with him. Why don't you get in a line?" Theodor directed the passengers, most of whom outmeasured his slender frame, even the women. "We're going to be together for a time, so we might as well make good use of the map. Besides, it will be nice knowing where we're all coming from."

Stefan spoke up. "But first let's find a good place to write." He spied a flat ledge and continued writing neatly the rest of the names in the German script of the time, while Theodor got the crowd into position according to the order he had seen them appear. Soon a few others came, and seeing the line, joined it. Everybody wanted to be on the map.

When Theodor saw that the passengers could carry on by themselves, he said to Stefan, "Adolf and I have to go down below a while. He still needs to take some *Underberg* and to rest."

"I'll save a place for you at supper then," Stefan said as the two departed. Adolf questioned Theodor's backward glance at the crowd. Theodor shrugged.

"*Geselligkeit,*" he said.

"*Ja,*" Adolf intoned wistfully, as if suddenly reminded of home. "Gregariousness indeed."

When later the supper gong sounded, Theodor and Adolf mounted the steps to the dining room. They arrived in line as Walter was perusing Stefan's map. "Look at that! The country has dots from all over. We're not just from my "German corner," but from every corner of Germany and beyond."

The Bodensee (*Lake Constance*) *showing surrounding countries and cities.*
(*Switzerland, Austria and Germany*)

Theodor scrutinized the map to find it was true. Not only was the land inside the border filled with dots, but also German-speaking enclaves in eastern Europe were represented. The Romanian Osterlands weren't the only ones. Adolf, who had just noticed the dot in Romania, asked, "Who are the Osterlands?"

"That was the father I was telling you about that I met on the wharf tending his children."

After supper they lingered at the table discussing the prospects for their remaining stay on board. Adolf had already been looking around and realized that Herr Kraenke had left. He took advantage of the absence to comment, "I hope Mr. Cranky regains his sense of humor soon. I don't look forward to listening to him during the whole trip." He thought he had said it softly, but Stefan next to them took up the cause. "Ja, at first I thought it was because he'd been sick." Stefan shifted his cap.

Jakob looked up a moment from his reading. "Maybe it's just that he's from the north. You know they have a reputation for austerity."

"Ja, maybe he's originally from Prussia," said Michael.

"Oh, no," Herr Grundig joined in. Assuming the lad was referring to the brusque manner and unilateral stance of the Prussian Kaiser Wilhelm II prior to the outbreak of the Great War, he added, "He's not militant, just grumpy."

Frau Seligmann realized that Frau Kummer had also departed "Then there's also Mrs. Worrywart." Surprised at the frankness that had escaped her, she surveyed her audience guiltily. But when Walter said, "Ja, then it's going to be a really long trip," she was relieved.

"Do you think we can stand it for the rest of the time?" Adolf asked.

Walter said, "It's something to think about. We don't have the luxury of the Titanic!"

Theodor's thoughts, however, had already been churning. The idea fomenting in his head had not quite shown where it was going, but soon it would consolidate itself.

Just then two children from the other sleeping quarters passed in front of them. They were the ages of Anni and Heini. They even resembled them somewhat, the first blond and blue-eyed and the second brunette, just like in their family. The sight filled the brothers with longing for their niece and nephew. They hadn't realized how much they missed the tykes, even though they were always making a nuisance of themselves. The two brothers couldn't resist relating their antics.

"When we got home from work they decided *we* should tend them instead of their mother," said Theodor.

"*Ja,*" said Adolf, "they were always asking for a glass of water right after we sat down."

"Or they wanted to sit on our laps when we wanted to rest a minute."

"Or read them a story just when we were ready to leave the house."

"You must miss them a lot," said Michael kindly.

"*Ja,* what we wouldn't give for a little inconvenience now, *richtig,* Theodor?"

Theodor, choked with nostalgia, finally managed to say, "The hard part is the thought that we'll probably never see our little ones again."

"*Meinst du?*" asked Walter. "*Ich weiß nicht.* I never thought I'd make a trip back."

Theodor knew he said it to cheer him up. Finally he said, "If we do, I'm afraid we won't recognize them, by then they'll be all grown-up."

KUNST ODER KITSCH?

Die Meersburg (*the Old Castle*)

The following morning at their breakfast of porridge, weak tea, and sugar, Theodor showed a picture post card of the Meersburg to his table companions.

"The castle in your home town?" Michael asked.

"*Jawohl!* The oldest castle in Germany." As his chest thrust outward so did his teacup.

"The oldest *inhabited* castle," corrected Adolf. "Dates back to A.D. 628. What's really remarkable is they had to bore through rock for water."

"*Erstaunlich!* It must have been breathtaking growing up under such a stronghold."

"*Das stimmt!*" Theodor said, staring pensively at the mighty fortress. "Anyway, I have an idea. We're going to be on board at least two more weeks. We might as well make them worth it."

"*Was hast du im Sinne, Theodor?*" Walter looked at Theodor curiously. Adolf ladled oatmeal into his mouth. "*Ja!* I want to know what you have in mind, too."

"I was just thinking that everybody has something they brought along to show their kin in America, maybe what the old home town looks like now, if it's nothing more than a post card. So why don't we show each other what we've brought?"

That noon after the lunch table had been cleared, they laid out the pictures they had collected during the morning. Jakob had one of the Frankfurter Court House as well as the Limes in a nearby area. Michael brought the famous Ulmer Cathedral, the Bayers, the Augsburger onion-towered church.[64] Frau Kummer had the Karolingian castle of *Karl des Großen* at Aachen and the Grundigs the university at Tübingen. That's when they learned that Herr Grundig had taught there.

"So you are really a Herr Professor," stated Michael. "Actually Herr Professor Doktor." But Herr Grundig, contrary to custom, shrugged off the title. Michael opened his mouth to say more, but by that time those from other tables had drawn close to the clamor.

When Herr Osterland saw the name Donaueschingen, he said, "Hey! Source of the Danube and we have the mouth—or mouths, should I say?"

"No kidding! From Romania? Where the Danube empties into the Black Sea?" asked Michael, who had the picture from a trip there.

"*Ja,* a series of shots actually. Why don't you get them for us?" Herr Osterland instructed one of his sons. A conversation had arisen among the throng, comparing the different cities through which the Danube flowed. As the boy departed, their fellow travelers, thinking of their own contributions, scurried away after him like mice after the pied piper of Hamelin, leaving the brothers to wonder what they might come up with.

Soon they were back, spreading out photos, paintings, and sketches.

They displayed Gothic cathedrals and Renaissance courthouses, scenic views of the Rhine and more of the Danube, the trees of the *Schwarzwald* and the Alps, as well as rivers and forests, valleys and hills near their hometowns. The names would not be known outside the area, but local people insisted on naming every geographical phenomenon. Some correlated towns with composers, such as Beethoven and Bonn, Mozart and Salzburg, Bach and Leipzig, Wagner and Bayreuth, or with artists, as Stefan Lang had done with photos of Albrecht Dürer's works from the museum in nearby Nuremberg. A picture of the artist's "Praying Hands" he intended for his nephews.

A mother-daughter couple, Frau and Fräulein Schwartz, had a picture of the old Roman portal, *Porta Nigra*, in their hometown of Trier near the French border. The two women were always dressed in black, making the rest think that the husband and father must have lost his life in the Great War. But such topics they avoided.

Of course, from time to time Herr Kraenke couldn't resist a derogatory remark, such as mentioning that mold actually accounted for the Black Gate's color in Trier. And when a young lady, her youthful face bright with enthusiasm, introduced herself as Fräulein Strom, Herr Kraenke demanded, "*Strom oder Storm?*" The way he pronounced the latter, it came out like *Sturm*. He hadn't meant it to be funny, but everyone laughed at what turned out to be a play on words.

Undaunted she retorted, "*Nein, Strom, Strom.*" Delft blue eyes sparkled beneath flaxen hair, limp but billowing tidily about her face. Her voice tinkled melodiously like a Solinger steel spoon against a Rosenthal porcelain cup.[65]

"Not a storm, but a stream or an electrical current perhaps." The Herr Professor Grundig's expression suggested mystery.

"*Genau!*" she sang back, casting him a grateful look. "The Strom family," she indicated her parents on either side of her, "from Stuttgart wants to talk to you about the Daimler Benz factory."

"*Ja, das Auto kommt,*" chimed in Frau Strom. Her husband said, "In the next few years the world is going to see the number of cars multiply."

"Do you have a Daimler Benz car?" asked Herr Kraenke.

"Of course not, but cars will get cheaper and every family will have one."

"I hear Bosch electrical, also in your city, is not hiring, *nicht wahr?*" maintained Herr Kraenke. His audience was puzzled by this bit of rare information, when at other times, he seemed so unknowledgeable about common things.

But Adolf chose to respond. "I have to back you up on that one. I applied at Bosch, but in vain."

Frau Kummer had sat silently, wringing her hands. Nevertheless, an abrupt change in attitude of the members showed up next morning. Instead of shuffling to breakfast, mouths gaping with yawns, they appeared wide awake, eagerly talking to people whose names they hadn't known the day before. That morning they were treated to everything from the Wartburg, where Martin Luther allegedly threw an

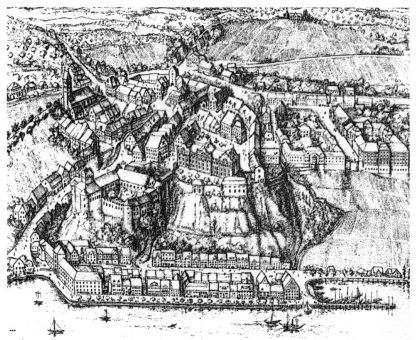

The old city of Meersburg with Upper and Lower Towns, drawn by Maria Kegel Maillard. Meersburg/ Bodensee, "Kultur und Veranstaltungen," Sept./Okt. 1987, p.12.

inkwell at the devil, to the charming Judengasse, with its quaint shops in Salzburg as well as to the fortress itself and on to the Pergamon Museum in Berlin. Adolf had dug out his picture of the zeppelin factory in Friedrichshafen from his short-term job there.

At lunch, Theodor asked, *"Was meint ihr?"* He indicated the array of pictures.

"I think we should continue along these lines," said Stefan immediately.

"But I think we will exhaust the picture series by this afternoon. How many such things can one take on a boat?" Frau Kummer was rubbing her hands together, while Herr Kraenke sat with a sour look.

Herr Bayer suddenly suggested, "Why don't we also share the gifts we brought for our sponsors?"

"Ach ja," said his wife. "Especially those articles typical of our hometown."

"Zweifellos! And we can all learn something about other parts of the homeland," said Michael.

Walter added, *"Großartig! Dort drüben* you are going to be bombarded with questions about the homeland. You should know something about the country as a whole, not just your own region. 'Over there in America' they think all Germany is either Bavaria or Prussia."[66]

Theodor hadn't thought of that. *"Gut!"* Nobody had voiced up to now the typical comparison popular since 1871, when Bismarck succeeded in forming the Second Reich, between the serious, progressive north and the fun-loving, if not sometimes quaint, south.

But Frau Kummer, reflecting on her own sparse specimens, objected to the whole idea. *"Ich weiß es nicht,"* she said, twining her fingers around. "We're sure to collect a lot of *kitsch.*"

"Richtig!" agreed Herr Kraenke. "Who wants to see other people's *schmalzy* show?"

"Herr Kraenke," *Hänschen* said accusingly, "and you didn't even bring a picture!"

Herr Kraenke shot a look at his parents as if to say, what are you going to do about him? He directed his glance particularly at the Frau

Professor who, after all, was supposed to be in charge of the three Ks.[67]

But Adolf had already countered, "Anyway there will be a story connected with the junk!"

"*Richtig!* The junk has to have a personal attachment for someone to bring it all the way to America," Walter said.

The Grundigs cinched the deal. "Art or junk—*das ist eine gute Idee!*"

The next morning after breakfast, Theodor primed the idea of bringing objects with carvings from his brother living in the Black Forest. The area reminded Frau Friedrich, a woman from Freiburg whom they had just met, that she had a good recipe she could pass on for *Schwarzwälderkirschtorte* made with Black Forest cherry liqueur. "And I also have the regional costume." Thus, others thought of their own possibilities.

An hour later they encountered a corner of the deck with an array of items. The Black Forest costume stood out because of the lady's straw hat festooned with red bumbles and the sash to tie under the neck. There were other regional costumes as well as figurines, books, plates, tapestries, linens, and various clothing articles. Those who hadn't brought anything to the table were further reminded of objects they could share. Of course, some of the pieces were pure *kitsch*, but again Little Hans saved the situation. "We have time for this. We're not going any place, are we?" The grown-ups around him smiled at his utterance. Someone said, "Out of the mouths of babes."

Other newcomers to the group came forward. The Mainzers, with a Bible in hand, reminded the audience of their native son Johann Gutenberg and how his invention of movable type enabled mass publication so that Luther in the next century was able to print his translation of the Bible in the vernacular. The Hamburgers brought a prewar picture of the Hamburg harbor when it was still the world's third largest seaport after New York and London. Now, of course, it had been displaced. So the morning went with a few more participants before they stopped for lunch.

One morning several days later, it, looked as if they were celebrating Christmas. The Nurembergers started the trend by bringing a glass-blown ornament from their *Christkindlmarkt*. The bauble reminded others of their articles from their Christ-child markets. People from Thüringen exhibited a hand-carved advent windmill from the pine forests of their native state east of Bavaria. The throng marveled at the intricate folk art of the nativity scene. They had heard about or seen in pictures such things, but for most it was the first personal witness of such handiwork. [68]

Evergreens with perky, carved branches curling upward, enveloped blessed figures in the center. When the couple lit the four candles, which set the wheel in motion around the delicately whittled wood, they marveled even more. Amid oohs and aahs the Thuringers explained that the blades placed at angles above caught the draft of the lit candles, causing the wheel to revolve. The husband could not resist. "You're reacting just like our children do." His wife pointed out that the little ones get a feeling for how long they have to wait until Christmas, as each week in Advent an additional candle from the previous week is lit.

As Theodor absorbed the delicate craftsmanship, he thought—no wonder the family said they needed more time. A crew member must have had to open a locker in order for them to retrieve the fragile piece. Afterwards they replaced its protective wrapping, a laborious process.

Meanwhile *Hänschen* Grundig wanted to know a bit of information to which Jakob had referred earlier. "Herr Friedman, what's the *Limes*, you know that place you were talking about not too far from where you live in Frankfurt?"

"The word's from Latin, *mein Kind*. It means 'limit.' It was the northern boundary of the Roman Empire a long time ago. *Und weißt du was?* You can still see the remains of walls and watchtowers," informed Jakob.

"You can?" The mention obviously intrigued the little guy.

"*Ja*, they're pretty dilapidated after so many years, but you can still see the outlines."

"*Ach, Mutti*," he turned to his mother, "we should go there."

She nodded, biting her lip. "*Ja, Liebchen*, someday we might."

That evening as they filed in to supper, Michael Baumgartner commented, "You know, I'm really glad we're doing these presentations.

You'd never know we had all this display among us."

Stefan nodded. "*Na ja*, I imagine that people have been so occupied with the aftermath of the Great War they haven't been able to spread local customs around."

"Although the soldiers should account for some exchange with other places," said Adolf.

Walter suddenly sat silently. He was remembering what Theodor had told him that the soldiers at the German front were saying, "Hell, we are the sacrifice!"

Nevertheless, each day of "show and tell" seemed to enliven the passengers a little more. They had gone much beyond learning each others' names. From snatches of conversation the brothers overheard, they found that many of them were exchanging useful information on the Old Country and the New Country. At lunch the sharing of personal stories continued animatedly around the plank tables.

On dark, rainy days the families huddled in the dining room, catching up on personal matters, like letters, diaries, and other records. Women took up their usual needlework and men whittled objects out of dainty pieces of pine. Children read or sang or played games. They all did the best they could in the meager space and candlelight.

Even sunny days were sometimes sedate, whereas others were boisterous. Both occurred when the Bavarians, a group larger than most, took their turn. The Einfalt family had so much they wanted to tell, especially about their capital, Munich, where they lived. How could the Einfalts not boast about the *Deutsches Museum*, one of the largest science and technology museums in the world? And what about the gigantic *Glockenspiel* that chimed regularly at eleven in the morning in their magnificent City Hall on Marian Square? Then there was the *Frauenkirche*, the Church of Our Lady, adjacent to the *Marienplatz*. By then they hadn't even covered their art museums or their parks. "How are we ever going to limit ourselves?" they said as they discussed their dilemma.

Herr Bayer thought their porcelain factories also deserved mention. But in the middle of the presentation on how the residue from cattle bones in the soil accounted for the whiteness of the area's porcelain, the atmosphere was interrupted by a voice from the audience, "*Sagen Sie uns mal über das Oktoberfest!*"

Attention immediately switched from what is called culture with a capital C to one with a little c.

"Yes, tell us once," his partner next to him demanded. "I'd like to know why it's called Oktoberfest, when it's in September."

At that point Herr Einfalt, sitting next to the Bayers, stood up. The audience suddenly realized that the hefty fellow had appeared in typical Bavarian costume. His *Lederhosen* revealed years of wear, the gray suede in some spots oiled smooth, the red cord trim cracked here and there, and the green leather trim showed bare spots. His hat with its wide feather sat jauntily on his head. Thick woolen knit bands exaggerated his muscular legs. Then his wife beside him stood, and the audience could see that she was clad Bavarian-style in a *dirndl*, with a striped blue skirt flaring out from a rose-colored, tight-fitting bodice, which made the stark white blouse billow about her bosom. Frau Einfalt spread in curtsy fashion the elaborately embroidered apron whose ties wound around her waist to end with a bow in front. She greeted bashfully, "*Grüß Gott!*"

Herr Einfalt continued, "Originally the beer festival was intended to commemorate a Bavarian princess' wedding, which was held in October. But later people decided that the month was too cold for such an annual outdoor memorial, so they moved it to September."

"It was even too cold with all that polka dancing?" Their compatriots took that as a signal to break in with an oom-pa-pa, mimicking drum and trumpet. The Einfalts began to polka. Others followed, including the Einfalts' son, who was dressed in short gray suede pants just like his father. The child dragged Frau Bayer onto a cleared spot. Soon the accompaniment lapsed into the *Schuhplattler*. When the time came for Herr Einfalt to slap his bare knees, Frau Einfalt circled around him, rotating all the while.

After a bit, the makeshift band stopped humming and drumming, whereupon the Bavarians led a *Dreimal hoch* toast. "Yes," Herr Einfalt affirmed, laughing jovially, "let's raise our glasses three times, just like in the *Hofbräuhaus*."

Herr Kraenke looked puzzled, so Walter explained, "They're not referring to just any beer hall, Herr Kraenke, but the great one in Munich, where the Oktoberfest is held—in September." Then he playfully poked him. "If we keep on like this in America, we're going to reinforce the idea to the locals that there is nothing in Germany between Bavaria and Prussia."

PLUMMETING POLEMICS

Elation, of course, was not a constant. Even though their animated stories often stretched into the lunch hour, the optimism could not always be sustained. The moments of anguish that erupted from time to time puzzled the voyagers. One moment they would be laughing and cajoling each other good-naturedly, the next they would be snarling at each other over some insignificant issue. Some attributed the bursts of anger to lack of rest. Admittedly it was not easy to sleep in a room full of people with someone coughing all night, someone snoring, someone punching an elbow into a rib, and most of all the babies crying in the next room where families slept. As the days wore on, the outbreaks appeared with increasing volatility, until one day an intense situation brought the activities to a complete stop right in the midst of a couple's exhibit.

Noisily the pair worked through a bulky bundle, as onlookers followed their laborious movements. "*Vorsicht, Wolfgang,*" his wife was saying. "We've gotten it this far, we can't break it now." The audience thought the object must be exceedingly fragile to warrant so much wrapping.

"*Ja, Gertrude,*" the husband answered. Finally they extracted from its plush packaging a tiny, delicate object of art, with a striking blue design against purest white. Suddenly the pair became aware of their audience. Embarrassed, the man muttered, "*Ach! Hallo!* We're the Krugs from the Dresden area." But he seemed unable to proceed. He was still groping for words when the Frau Professor Grundig—the form of address for a wife with her husband's title—suggested, "You have a piece perhaps from *Meißen?*"

"Why, yes," Herr Krug stuttered. "How did you know?

The Frau Professor smiled. "Because *Meißen* is just outside Dresden and it has a famous porcelain factory."

"*Ja, ja,* that's what we wanted to show you—the piece of *Meißener* china we're bringing as a gift to our sponsors in America." [69]

They held up the object and the audience saw a tiny pitcher, the size of a single creamer, with the famous blue onion pattern. A strange sound seemed to pierce the atmosphere but it was soon lost in the crowd's enthusiasm. The Herr Professor Grundig, intent on the object, said, "Turn it over, so we can see the *Meißen* symbol." Frau Krug did so, but without letting go the precious item. "This is the current official blue trademark. The Herr Professor is right. Because the trademark design is changed every so often, one can determine the approximate age of a piece by the variation in its symbol, but the mark is usually some type of crossed swords, and . . . "

Suddenly a cry wrenched the atmosphere, and this time there was no mistaking that it was human. The crowd sought the source and found Frau Osterland sobbing against her husband's shoulder.

"*Was ist los?*" people asked her husband, ready to help.

"*Nichts, nichts,*" he shrugged.

"Nothing's the matter?" Frau Kummer's wringing hands were busy in front of her chest.

Meanwhile Frau Osterland cried even harder. Her children began pommeling her with questions, "*Warum weinst du, Mutti?*" "*Tut es dir weh?*" "*Bist du krank?*"

Finally Herr Osterland said, "She's neither hurt nor sick, *meine Kinder.*" To the crowd he said, "She's just thinking of all the things we left behind. She didn't want to leave our home, you know." Frau Osterland kept muttering, "Crossed swords . . . crossed swords . . . " And just before they led her away, she muttered, "Strange combinations . . . " The spectators thought that *Meißen* china must have held a special meaning in her family.

No sooner had they departed than those inhabitants from the *Ruhrgebiet* picked up on her despair. They had all along been observing in silence as others showed off their enterprising endeavors. But what did they have to show from their region, from Solingen, from Düsseldorf, from Wuppertal, Essen, Münster and other Ruhr cities? They couldn't imagine what they should do when their turn came. Their region was famous for its stainless steel carving sets, especially those with bone handles. But what came foremost in their minds nowadays was not the source of pride from the old days but rather the painful reminder of a land laid low.

Herr Braun among them, could not stem his feelings any longer and let go with a diatribe that must have been building for some time. With each statement he paused, and the next came out with more vehemence. "I've worked more than thirty years in the steel industry. As a boy in the eighties, I saw it develop. When I went to work in the nineties, I helped build it up. At the turn of century, I saw it grow. As an old man I saw it flourish. And what have I to show for it? No pension, not even a month's salary to tide me over, nothing. . . . " By now his shoulders shook and his voice quivered. "Not even a certificate of appreciation." The last he almost whispered.

In his state of agitation he could hardly place his rough, reddened hands over his mottled face. His wife approached to slip her hand through the crook of his arm. His grandson covered the old man's hands with his own, saying, "*Komm, Opa.*" The two pulled him gently away. Women and children watched the retreating figures in horror, while husbands and fathers moved to block the view between their charges and the disgrace.

Nevertheless, his outburst forced to the fore the trauma that plagued them all. Were they escaping from the Old Country, or were they pursuing a dream in the New? Deep down the emigrants carried their own precarious feelings, especially those of betrayal to their relatives, to their country. None of them was on this ship without the sacrifice of those left behind, which even included help toward payment of tickets.[70] Were they abandoning their homeland in its most downtrodden time?

Theodor looked around helplessly for a way to salvage the situation. At last he made a decision. "Let's stop here and tomorrow . . . and tomorrow we'll continue, then . . . then we'll have a quiz on who's from where, and what its importance is." The crowd hardly laughed at his feeble attempt at lightheartedness. "Yes, yes," he concluded weakly, "we should be able to talk more about our country than just our own region."

The next day, however, they failed to follow his suggestion. Someone had brought to breakfast a photo album, a family treasure that up to now no one had considered showing. They had previously insisted to themselves that it was something they had intended primarily for their American relatives. Albums contained far too intimate events to share with complete strangers. Or were they avoiding something?

Others followed suit, and soon the passengers had fallen into groups of two, three, four, or five. In the end, the present turned out to be the appropriate time. Careworn, expressionless faces softened as they talked about their families in the photos, which inevitably ended with grieving the loss of someone dear in the war effort. Vocabulary arose in paradoxical twosomes, such as village and rubble, virility and vomit, food and excrement, walls and blood. Even if one had no direct experience with destructive forces on the environment, graphic details played on the mind. And by the way, what had Frau Osterland meant when she labeled "crossed swords" as a strange combination? In any event, they realized there was no one who could not talk about some casualty, some atrocity, some horrible memory burned into the brain.

After supper that evening, Herr Kraenke's odd posture made the others wonder if he was holding something behind his back. Michael finally asked, "What do you have there, Herr?" He was indeed guarding something, but now he seemed loathe to bring it forward. At last his position became so awkward that he drew his hand from behind. The throng saw a photo of the *Lüneburger Heide*, from his area in the north. The moorland, purple with heather, brought exclamations at its beauty. But some looked on questioningly, suspecting more to the heath's significance than its geographical phenomena.

Finally Herr Kraenke managed a couple of words. "My wife . . . " The pause was so long that someone inserted, "Yes, Herr Kraenke, your wife?"

The minute it was said, the crowd drew in its breath as if all thinking alike. Why hadn't she accompanied him? Why wasn't she on the boat? Was he going on ahead to send her transportation money later? Then Herr Kraenke set them straight. "My wife . . . is buried there."

Frau Seligmann gasped. "Oh, Herr Kraenke, we're so sorry . . . " Why had it not occurred to her that the poor man was suffering internally? She had heard someone ask him whether he had been in the war, and by his nonchalant affirmation, she hadn't given it another thought. Along with fellow passengers she thought him cranky, but completely composed. Reconsidering, however, Frau Seligmann did find his facial muscles rather taut. Oh, I should have questioned further! she scolded herself.

But now the distraught widower had lost control of his emotions. His cheeks sagged, his shoulders slumped, and he said in staggered snatches, "I was home from the battle lines . . . I had been wounded . . . I was sent home to recover . . . my wife tended my wounds." He was now rubbing his chest. Flashing through Frau Seligmann's mind was that it was a familiar gesture. Of course, he was massaging his wounds! "There was a stray bomb." Even though the words "men don't cry" were gnawing at him from the past, he broke down before he said, "She died in my arms." By that time Frau Seligmann was holding him. At last he said, "Wish I had been taken with her."

"Of course you do." Frau Seligmann patted his arm, thinking—odds were that Herr Kraenke was trying to escape his loss by going to the New Country, but now he was finding out that he carried his sorrow with him. Poor Herr Kraenke, she told her husband that night, and they agreed. The man had recovered physically from the war but not emotionally.

As the arrival grew more imminent, sadness and guilt at what they had left behind began to weigh on them all. They suddenly realized that *das Alte Land*, the Old Country, held haunting memories of destruction, even loss of life and land dear to them, and they were not going to disappear just because *das Neue Land*, the New Country, was now their home. It was not a matter of merely changing outer geography but of clinging to inner geography, that of their hopes and dreams, their fortitude and persistence, their industriousness and expertise—in short, their Old World skills. They had talked to each other about their families and their occupations and their dreams for the future. What did Walter call it? Entrepreneurship, something like that. They would need their Old World skills and dreams to survive in the New World. That would be their contribution, and it would soften the blow for having to leave the Old World.

Meißen porcelain trademark 1815-1924

NEBULOUS NECROSIS

The shattered man spent the next day in the company of the Seligmanns in a secluded corner of the deck. A wind had come up, and every now and then it carried a word or two to those clustered across from them on the other side of the deck. Words such as: " . . . the one left . . . " " . . . live on . . . " " . . . dead in life . . . " seemed liked phrases typical of the Seligmanns.

The others took in as much as they could, before their own emotions on the subject took control. But they shifted their focus to their country's foreign policy, jumping from one subject to another, each according to a personal grave grievance. "This has been coming for a long time . . . *Jawohl!* Like when we thought we had to have colonies just like the other countries . . . . scraps of territory and insignificant islands which the colonial powers no longer wanted. . . . As the saying goes, 'trading a pair of pants for a pants button'. . . . Besides that we were involved in all those territorial conflicts in Morocco. . . . *Ja,* and we only succeeded in getting everyone mad at us. . . . *Richtig!* War almost broke out back then. . . . Don't forget the Balkan crises in the other direction. . . . *Genau!* The so-called 'urge toward the East'. . . . *Stimmt's!* The Berlin to Baghdad railroad scheme. . . . In the meantime Germany is getting more powerful on the seas. . . . It's no wonder the Triple Entente came about. . . . Supposedly the treaty was a mere defensive alliance, in case of aggression. . . . *Natürlich!* France and Britain felt pressured to become allies, but what were we to think when Russia became the third party? . . . *Stimmt's!* An aggressive move, enclosing us between the traditional major powers . . . a *Pufferstaat* between the western and eastern European civilizations. . . . Mutual distrust was increasing. . . . "

With a *na ja* the majority of them left, shrugging as if the search for answers were hopeless. Staying behind were the Grundigs, the brothers, and Walter. Karl Sachsen, usually in Walter's vicinity, had also left, saying he had to prepare for his meetings that would come up in New York soon after disembarkation.

The other five looked at each other, as if there were much more to say, yet not finding the words. Finally the Herr Professor Grundig spoke. "Mishandling of affairs took place among all the nations concerned, although most do not see it that way. Yet I think in future years it will be widely accepted that Europe had indeed been a powder keg, entrenched in defensive alliances, secret treaties, broken promises . . . " He looked at the others, who looked back at him, as if expecting him to elaborate. Finally he said, "The things said a moment ago all have some truth, but they are recent references. I think trouble was brewing farther back than 1871."

Walter was looking at the others blankly.

Adolf filled in. "That's the year when Prussia finally unified the German states—north and south, to become the Second Reich."

Turning to the professor, Theodor asked in a curious tone, "*Was meinen Sie?*"

The Herr Professor paused a long time before he said, "I don't have all the answers. But the way I see it, a great source of Germany's difficulties has to do with its role in European history. First, we need to remember that up until the end of the nineteenth century, or let's say for all practical purposes, up to our lifetime, Germany had little status among its European neighbors." The Herr Professor braced himself for the counter thoughts the others would likely want to raise, and blurted, "I'm not referring to fields like literature, music, art, philosophy, and so on, where we have for a long time had worldwide cultural acclaim."

Walter brightened at the familiar link. "Even I know about Goethe and Schiller, and the three B's—Beethoven, Bach and Brahms—not to mention the philosopher Kant, and even Mozart."

The Herr Professor acknowledged, "That may well be the source of a great reputation. However, I'm talking about the lack in Germany's political power especially among the traditional major European powers. The Holy Roman Empire was not keeping up with other European nations. Spain, England, and France had centralized governments with capitals well-established already during medieval times. [71] Their drive in the sixteenth century for overseas colonies, moreover, put them in an advantageous position. [72]

"Das verstehe ich nicht," said Walter. "How does that play a role?"

Now the Frau Professor Grundig rushed to help their German-American travel companion understand. "When those countries made their colonial conquests, Germany was not a seafaring nation, a shortcoming in its foreign policy. Because it never participated in acquiring land overseas, later on it had no outlet for surplus populations or for access to new markets."

 Empire of Charlemagne 814 *(beginning of the Holy Roman Empire)*
Original possessions and acquisitions

⊙ Aachen - Charlemagne's capital
⊙ Cordova - Capital of the Arabian Emirate in 814

118

The Herr Professor continued. "All along there had been continuous tension with France, which had always had its eye on the left bank of the Rhine. During the seventeenth century under Louis XIV this tension became critical.[73] Then came changes in military tactics brought on through the French Revolution in 1789, which emboldened Napoleon Bonaparte some twenty years later to take French imperialism a step further.[74] Soon he had gained control over much the same territory as the Holy Roman Empire. In fact, Napoleon's regime is often called the reenactment of that First German Reich. He even had himself crowned before the pope like *Charlemagne* in 800."[75]

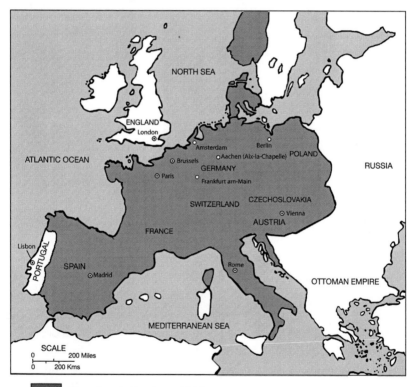

Napoleon's Empire – 1815 *(sometimes called the reenactment of the Holy Roman Empire)*

Territory under direct rule of or subject to Napoleon
⊙ Capitals, Vienna was the last capital of the Holy Roman Empire; notice that Berlin was not a capital
○ Other cities included for orientation purposes

"*Ach, ich verstehe,*" Walter said, after thinking a moment.

"*Jawohl!*" The Herr Professor nodded to Walter. "Unfortunately, after the fall of the Empire, the numerous principalities surviving that Thousand Year Reich competed with each other for pomp and power. Although a German Confederation[76] was formed, the various princes were too enamored with their self-importance to sacrifice toward a national political unity. The established countries did not have a high opinion of the German Confederation despite its other achievments."

Walter looked as if he were rearranging data in his mind. Stefan reminded them of the interim event, the Revolution of 1848, which was when his relatives fled for their lives to America.

"*Genau!*" said the Herr Professor. "It wasn't as if a liberal[77] element never existed. But it was always thwarted from gaining control one way or another. Up until the latter part of the last century, Germany was considered a minor, even quaint, European power."[78]

Walter appeared dumfounded again. "But, Herr Professor, Germany had such educational prestige. Many Americans were sending their children to your universities or just to get their horizons broadened."

"Among other countries," the Herr Professor reminded. "From an American standpoint the scene probably looks much different than it actually was."

Walter still looked perplexed.

"You're thinking of Germany as it stood in recent years under Prussia. But Europe saw Prussia rise as a political threat to them.[79] Even Prussia's rise to a European power didn't happen until the eighteen sixties when Kaiser Wilhelm I and Bismarck forged the North German Confederation, with Prussia, of course, as the dominant state. About the same time the French were losing confidence in their leader Napoleon III because he had made some embarrassing political decisions. Next comes the Franco-Prussian War, in which Bismarck, through political maneuvering, managed to gain the support of the south German states, which had been previously sympathetic to France. Thus was born the Second Reich, and the north and south German states were at last united under the leadership of Prussia."[80]

Adolf spoke up. "Mother always regarded Bismarck highly, *nicht wahr*, Theodor?"

"Because of his statesmanship?" Walter also asked, not sure of Bismarck's reputation.

"Mostly because of the social legislation for the common person that we talked about earlier."

"I think most Germans admired the Chancellor," said Stefan. "I remember my family saying nobody even minded that Austria wasn't included in the Second Reich, because things were going so well."[81]

"There was something about an early economic boom, followed by a crash, which surprised everybody because it stabilized,"[82] said Michael.

"*Richtig!* Something else outsiders didn't expect. That period of fifty years when Germany was politically floundering, the other fronts that were nonetheless succeeding, were not limited to the fine arts. The country made great economic strides in industrialization and railroad construction," said the Frau Professor.[83]

Adolf and Theodor played off each other, one giving names, the other coming back with products: "Siemens . . . electricity . . . Krupp and Thyssen . . . coal and iron . . . Zeiss . . . lenses."

"Besides all the inventions that were flourishing by then—telegraph, telephone, automobile," said Stefan.

"*Jawohl!*" said the Herr Professor. "We were not only blessed with geniuses at the helm of our factories, the workers also caught on to the concept of production and marketing, and with the consolidation of its political and economical powers, Germany's rise to a world power was established."[84]

The Frau Professor added, "In the 1890s things improved even further. By 1900 production had tripled and national income doubled."[85]

Walter stammered, "*Um Gottes willen!* I never thought of Germany as being a late bloomer. So not only is Germany, as a nation, younger than America, having been founded almost a century later, it seems the two were rising together to a strategic position in world affairs."

Stefan thought a moment. "You could say that. Certainly Europe never thought of America as a world power until it entered the Great War."

"But Germany's success contained within it the seeds of failure," said the Herr Professor.

"What are you saying?" asked Walter.

"That to the up-to-then great nations, we had suddenly become an upstart neighbor." The Herr Professor shrugged. "We hadn't paid our dues."

"Aha!" Walter replied after minute, "kind of like the feelings that arise when the kid brother comes along knowing how to operate the family business better than the big brother."

The Grundigs nodded. "Among other things."

"Like?"—the five lads said almost simultaneously.

"Like what I referred to earlier. Germany's historical development and geographical location and population growth."

"*Stimmt's!*" Walter remembered. "The buffer state position and the lack of colonies . . . "

"Yes," said the Frau Professor, "its key location squeezed between two power blocs, its surplus population, and lack of new market outlets . . . " [86]

"*Genau, Frau Professor!* That's why we were suddenly buying or trading for colonies, even though they didn't provide much help," said Adolf, as if he were putting the facts together for the first time.

"*Genau!* We were desperate, and thought—if colonies worked for the others, maybe they would for us too. But then something else happened, a change in leadership. Wilhelm II, who took over from his father in 1888, had neither the experience nor the stature of his father."

Theodor added, "And his awkwardness in managing the new empire grated on others."

The Herr Professor nodded. "Furthermore, the young emperor came under the influence of his uncle who was from the old school." [87]

"The idea that the monarchy is in charge, no questions asked?" said Stefan.

"Yes, sir! The monarchy traditionally demanded, negotiating was considered a sign of weakness," declared Michael, as if he, too, were understanding the situation better.

"German politics was still very much *in der K. und K. Zeit,*"[88] maintained the Frau Professor. "The monarchy still had a tight hold on governmental decisions, whereas other major monarchical countries had relaxed their control by enlisting other governing bodies."

"Nonetheless, even though Bismarck was iron-willed and clever, he was not foolhardy. He approached foreign policy for the most part cautiously,"[89] said the Herr Professor Grundig. "The young emperor, on the other hand, was too eager to prove Germany's prowess, too zealous to flaunt Germany as a major power, too anxious to partake in the stature of Europe. It took but two years until the inexperienced emperor asked for his chancellor's resignation.[90] The young czar's impetuousness and glory-seeking became even more intense without Bismarck there to counteract his intemperances.[91] Still it took almost ten years before the Kaiser's so-called 'new course' of German foreign policy showed its imperialistic tendencies."

Walter sat back a moment. "A kind of overreach like Napoleon a century before?" The Grundigs raised their eyebrows. Walter added, "And nowhere was it more evident than in the *Flottenbau, nicht wahr?*" His colleagues turned to stare at him. "That I could keep track of in the newspapers," defended Walter. "The way Wilhelm II built up the fleet of ships would have antagonized anybody."

"*Ja,* the crucial blow came when he challenged England's title as 'mistress of the seas.' That provoked unrest not only in England, but it intimidated all Europe," said the Herr Professor.[92]

"Whatever happened to Austria?" Walter asked.

"*Ach,* that's a long story!" the Herr Professor maintained. "But as far as the Second Reich is concerned, Austria was perhaps Bismarck's main weakness. He could not tolerate competition from another strong state. Since he preferred a 'Smaller Germany,' that is, without Austria rather than a 'Greater Germany' with Austria, is why some say that Bismarck was the destroyer of German unity."[93]

"Trouble had been going on for quite a while between the two dominant German powers, *nicht wahr?*"[94] Walter asked.

The Herr Professor spoke again. "*Ja,* the phenomenon is called Austrian-Prussian dualism. Back in the seventeenth century, when

Prussia produced its series of strong leaders, Austria was raised to a Great Power."[95]

"*Wirklich?*" Walter was perplexed. "How did that happen?" The others, who had learned the facts at one time, also listened intently in order to refresh their memories.

"It started with Louis XIV in the seventeenth century invading the left bank of the Rhine, the territory known as the Rhenish Palatinate, and ended with a treaty uniting Austria and Hungary. The European powers thought that Louis was overextending himself." The professor shrugged.

"Oh, so Napoleon's expansionism was not the first attempt at French imperialism in recent history?" Walter asked, as the facts sunk in.

"*Richtig!* And that was also a kind of overreach, to use your word, Herr Verwalter," his wife suggested. "On the other hand, Austria-Hungary had considerations which made it hesitate from joining Prussia. It was not only German-speaking, but contained Slavic- and Hungarian-speaking populations within its borders, neither of which it wanted to sacrifice, nor did Prussia want to accept."

Her husband continued, "The Austro-Hungarian Empire at that time had a dual monarchy, and by its refusal to go to a federation, Austria lost a golden opportunity."[96]

The Frau Professor continued the exchange of conversation with her husband. "In the meantime with Germany rising as a world power[97] under Prussia, that eastern coastal state began negotiating with other countries with the intention of defense against France."[98]

"In other words, trying to break its hegemony," the Herr Professor continued. "Nevertheless, when the Austrian Archduke, heir to the throne in Austria-Hungary, was assassinated in the Serbian city of Bosnia,[99] Germany rushed to the aid of its Austrian ally. After the Great War, Austria's Slavic and Hungarian minorities reversed their position and declared their independence from Austria. The German-speaking nation was at last ready to be part of 'Greater Germany,' but this time the Allied Powers prohibited the unification."[100]

"Everything was still all right in 1918 at the close of the war when we thought the treaty was going to be according to Wilson's Fourteen Points."[101]

Walter shook his head. "But Germany had asked for an armistice earlier, *nicht?*"

"Well, yes, but the Allied Powers didn't take the Germans seriously."[102]

"Or didn't want to," said Michael.

"By that time the casualities were already enormous,"[103] voluteered Stefan.

Walter still acted as if he were hearing the facts for the first time. "So what happened after that?"

The professor's face showed incredulity. "The Treaty of Versailles[104] upped the ante from the pre-armistice agreement that the Germans had signed."

"You mean, Woodrow Wilson's Fourteen Points, Herr Professor?" Walter confirmed.

The others nodded. The Herr Professor spoke to Walter's question. "It was incomprehensible, because German troops had already peacefully withdrawn from foreign lands by the end of November. The exorbitant reparations in machines and livestock were carried out in short order.[105] But negotiation over the Treaty went on until May of the following year. And still the food blockade went on."[106]

"*Ja,* I've never been able to figure out what the Allied Powers wanted," Theodor said. The other young men joined in. The amount to be paid was unreasonable. As far as any of them knew, no war indemnity had ever reached such an astronomical figure.[107] Moreover, they wondered, what would become of Wilson's Fourteen Points?[108]

Meanwhile Jakob Friedman had gone off by himself, mostly absorbed in his own thoughts. Still, the words of the others echoed in his ears, especially those of the Herr Professor Grundig. The tension in national politics had reached the common people. There was no doubt that all Europe had become so enmeshed in defensive alliances, which merely mirrored the growing distrust the countries felt for each other. Jakob, too, was of the opinion that European unrest had begun long before war's outbreak in 1914. In fact, he wasn't even sure any more whether wars were separate incidents or if there was only a single war, one war being merely an outgrowth of the last. Maybe dissatisfaction and resentment of one war held over until it escalated into the next. He hoped that 1918 really was the end of war, the "war to end all wars" in the words of Wilson. But he had little faith in its happening. He did not see the League of Nations able to provide effective leadership when it had no agency to enforce compliance.

In any case, although the war was formally ended, he saw Europe as still living under warlike conditions. The treaties had been signed, the troop withdrawal peacefully executed, stipulations for materials, livestock, farm and naval equipment satisfied, territorial properties confiscated, financial obligations pronounced, yet the displaced, the handicapped, the shell-shocked, the starving, the widowed, the unemployed were still with us and would be for a long time, not only for us, of course, but for all Europe. Reconstruction had barely begun, not to mention those on farms or in small businesses who managed to pull through whole in body and family, but who nevertheless were still left with anger, grief, and bewilderment. Since coming on board, Jakob realized how pervasive these feelings were. He, too, wondered about Wilson's Fourteen Points. Would they dissipate like the objectives of the peace movements?[109] Moreover, what was happening on the industrial front, Jakob thought, was just adding to an untenable situation. Labor was becoming nothing more than an object to man the machine in the factory. Gone was the artisan's pride in his accomplishment, his independence, and his *Gemeinschaft* with fellow craftsmen. Those who achieved recognition nowadays were those who willingly submitted to authority, honored efficiency, and endured long, monotonous hours, because they saw their gain linked to quantity rather than to quality— in short, persons who were committed to the production ideal and the profit motive.

Many current scholars alluded to factory workers as mere mechanical robots—industry sought machines to run the machines. The author that piqued Jakob's curiosity most on such social critique was Heinrich Mann. His recent novel *Der Untertan*, which Jakob preferred to think of as *The Underling* in English,[110] portrayed the effect of industrialization on factory personnel. Among other themes the story dealt with the effect of rivalry between a bourgeois couple over rearing their child. The son and main character, Diederich Heßling, was heir to the father's factory in the appropriately named village of Netzig. Jakob often just called it "Caught-in-a-Net."

Diederich had been groomed from infancy for his job as factory owner. As a child he received regular punishment for his indiscretions from his father. The latter was concerned about the influence of the mother, who whiled away far too much time reading novels and the weekly throwaways, so much so that on some days she didn't even finish her housework. The father believed it was up to him to impart strength and backbone to his offspring.

Jakob found the main character hateful and despicable, which his surname indicated, since it was related to *hassen,* to hate. Yet the deplorable personage managed to give others the illusion of standing on his own two feet. In the end, however, the story had Jakob asking, who is the true underling? Moreover, the story was reminiscent of the prophets of old in the Bible, denouncing the monarchy for its excesses at the expense of the masses, who had little recognition in the kingdom. The socio-political structure strangled the heart of the common people with a legalism so stringent that they were suffocating from it. As a result, their ability to express compassion or to act spontaneously became undermined for fear of authority catching them in an act of disobedience.[111]

But information had started blurring in Jakob's mind. He had to get it sorted out. Maybe in America his thinking would clear. He had long told himself, because of Europe's uncertain future, I want to study for my doctorate in an American university, preferably on the East Coast. From there I can easily keep track of European politics and at the same time have the freedom and the time to pursue my ideas and perhaps, he smiled to himself, even waste my time reading senseless things like poetry and novels once in a while, like Diederich's mother in Mann's novel.

EPISODE SIXTEEN

REVERBERATING RECOVERY

The day of the spectacle, the group had broken up as amicably as could be expected. Frau Seligmann found herself leaving the group alongside a man who, she had just learned, was from Cologne. "Herr Bischoff," she said, "why don't you do something godly?" She was thinking—that was not exactly their taste, her and her husband's, yet it just might be what was needed now. At all cost they wanted to avoid mention of the steel mills, at least for a while.

"Godly?" He gave her a perplexing glance.

"*Ja,* your cathedral."

"Oh, you mean *that* godly."

"Until now we haven't heard from you, *nicht wahr?*"

"*Richtig!* I didn't know what to do."

"*Ich hab' eine Idee.* It might be appropriate right now."

"*Gut!* Let's hear your idea."

"Remember when the Herr Offizier Niederung did his pantomime?" She reminded him how the crewman, when passing by their entertainment one day, had entered into the fun by acting out four different animals, piled up on each other's back, each playing a musical instrument. When he had asked, *Welche Stadt?* Herr Kraenke had echoed gruffly in return, "What city? What city?" But Hans had shouted gleefully, that was easy, it was Bremen. Remember, Herr Bischoff, how Hans said, '*Das sind doch die Bremer Stadtmusikanten.*'? Well, I was thinking something along those lines might work, Herr Bischoff."

After an interruption of a few days, when Theodor asked who was next, Herr Bischoff and his wife rose immediately. But they remained silent, motioning the onlookers to do likewise. They paced to and fro a moment, then motioned everyone to watch closely. The crowd followed as they formed tall thin triangles with their fingers, then they motioned opening a door, walking through it, and shutting it behind them. They knelt and put their hands together in praying position. But the spectators shook their heads in bewilderment. What did they want? The unexpected pantomime baffled them.

However, when Herr Bischoff repeated his act, Stefan Lang yelled, "*Natürlich! Der Kölner Dom! Die Stadt Köln!*"

"Naturally," the actors said, "the Cologne Cathedral." Was there any more famous church in Germany?

"Of course," Frau Bayer affirmed. "The tall spindly triangles represent the pointed towers of its Gothic architecture."

"*Richtig!*" the Kölner said.

"*Ausgezeichnet, Herr und Frau Bischoff!*" finalized Theodor. Their act started a trend for those who followed. The next afternoon, Theodor noticed people getting together in small groups, buzzing among themselves but going silent whenever people approached. "*Was ist jetzt los?*" he wondered. Though he couldn't figure out what was going on, he had to admit that the emigrants were miraculously regaining their optimistic mood from the earlier part of the trip.

At their next meeting Theodor began, "Well, here we are again, waiting to see your displays." Herr Volkmuth, whom they were just getting to know, rose and responded, "Oh, it's a display you want, a show? Well, compatriots, how about it? Shall we give it to them?" He had organized quite a group and now they responded with a resounding *JA!*

The audience perked up. Hand in front of mouth, Herr Volkmuth motioned silence. The act seemed perfect for him, who had not been very vocal up to now. The audience stopped talking. Then others from the group came forward. One bounced about like a little girl, apparently gathering something from the ground. Her eyes grew large with horror as she met another person, and mimed what big eyes, what big ears, what big teeth, what a big nose. The second person snapped at her.

Hans said, "*Ich weiß, ich weiß! Rotkäppchen und der Wolf!*" The group nodded. Then the people stiffened, half-expecting Herr Kraenke to yell, "*Ich verstehe nicht!* There's a monument to Little Red Riding Hood in your city?" But since his session with the Seligmanns, though his behavior was at times still abrasive, he had calmed down a great deal. Frau Osterland still had her sniffles during the demonstrations, but mostly they were so muffled that even those next to her were unaware of her silent tears. As for Frau Kummer they doubted she would ever succeed in quieting her hands.

When the onlookers couldn't get the city, the actors motioned to watch another couple. They acted out dropping something behind them and assuring themselves of the fact. They outlined a house, which they nibbled on. A third person opened the door of the make-believe house and couldn't resist breaking the silence in a dry, quaking tone, "*Wer knuspert an mein Häuschen?*" When Hans uttered "*Hänsel und Gretel,*" nobody argued. That was indeed the folktale where children nibbled on the witch's house. Still they had no clue as to the city. Then the actors held up thumb, index and middle fingers.

"Number three," interpreted Michael Baumgartner.

This time the players marched to and fro, wielding something on their shoulders, rounding their lips in whistling motion. "*Sieben!* There are seven persons." They had enlisted partakers among the audience. Hans' childlike fervor could no longer contain itself. "*Natürlich! 'Die Sieben Zwerge.'*"

Fräulein Strom reiterated, "Hmm. 'The Seven Dwarves,' 'Little Red Riding Hood,' 'Hansel and Gretel.'" Suddenly her eyes widened. "Oh, I get it. *Volksmärchen der Brüder Grimm.*"

"*Natürlich,*" the Bayers beamed. "The Grimm Brothers' Folk Tales."[112]

The audience noted that Herr Kraenke, who would have formerly thrown up his hands in frustration when they couldn't get the city, was still watching calmly.

"The birthplace of the Grimm Brothers—what city is that?" peeped Frau Kummer. She was wringing her hands as if faced with a test as serious as the *Abitur*.[113] The elder Grundigs were absent as well as Jakob Friedman. Herr Osterland and children were shaking their heads. So were the Seligmanns. Michael Baumgartner and Stefan Lang looked at each other blankly. Even Walter's forehead was creased in thought.

Nobody was coming up with the city, but since Herr Volkmuth deemed it was not a major one, he took pity. "*Ich weiß nicht, aber ich weiß doch, daß ich Kassler Rippchen liebe.*"

"Hm-m," shouted Stefan Lang "He loves smoked pork chops, which supposedly come from Kassel."

"*Es muß Kassel sein,*" said Michael Baumgartner in mock triumph.

Herr Volkmuth added, "It not only must be, it is. And it has a museum that contains a lot about the brothers collecting the fairy tales among common folk."

The ocean voyage was nearing its end, and it was time for the last act. A family of four, introducing themselves as the Spielbergs, had requested they be last for some reason. Theodor wondered if they had something special in mind. Indeed, it looked as if they were going to present a skit. For the first scene they had obtained some old kitchen sacks. The two children had cut a few holes in them.

When the father, as the owner of the sacks, began to take them away, tiny objects thudded from the holes against the wooden deck. As the man walked away, he noticed the sacks always getting lighter to carry. That's when he spied the two would-be urchins, played by his children. He pounced upon them and shoved them into the sacks. The squirming objects he took to the miller, played by his wife. She threw the contents of the sacks into a machine, a couple of chairs they had rigged together. The "miller" ground up the contents with an improvised handle. Then she put the contents back into the sacks, all the time referring to them as wonderful ground-up flour. Upon arriving home the owner spread the contents on the ground and something came and gobbled them up. Halfway through the portrayal *Hänschen* was already crying out, "*Ich weiß!*" But the Frau Professor held her fingers to her lips. "*Nichts sagen!*"

But Hans cried once more, "Aber ich!" His mother cautioned, "Let the others have a chance first, *mein Liebchen.*"

But no one took advantage, so Herr Spielberg resorted to Hans, who gleefully related the seventh and last prank of *Max and Moritz,* a comic cartoon known to every child. He told how the rascals were eventually ground up at the mill and fed to the geese in sweet justice for all the mischief they had caused to unsuspecting adults.[114]

But the presentation was not complete. Herr and Frau Professor Grundig volunteered Wilhelm Busch as the author.

"*Aber die Stadt?*" asked the Spielbergs.

They shook their heads. "*Das wissen wir leider nicht.*" Finally Frau Spielberg said, "*Gut!* By the way, what's the name of our ship again?"

Hans raised his hand eagerly. "The *Hannover.*"

"*Richtig!* That's it," she said.

"Okay," said Frau Kummer, "that's the ship, but what's the city?" There was a smile that ran through the crowd. She seemed to be taking up Herr Kraenke's former position.

"That's the answer!" For a child so young, Hans was exasperated.

Walter nudged the two brothers. "Remember that saying, 'That's the way the little Moritz imagines it?'"[115]

"*Ja,* the cartoon must be where the expression comes from."

"*Ja,* to mean a simplistic interpretation of a complicated situation."

"Which is all too often the case," summed up Jakob Friedman, who had just joined them.

As the audience broke up, Stefan said to his friends nearby, "That was the final show!"

"*Jawohl!* And I think we all came out with a better idea of our geography," added Michael.

"*Ja,* I learned so many new things," said Stefan. As they neared the end of their voyage across the Big Pond, the group discovered they were no longer just passengers occupying the same ship for a time. They had not only shared their joys, they had also shared their sorrows. They had experienced tragic circumstances, scenes for the most part that their American counterparts might never have seen, at least not on their own soil, and would probably therefore not take the time to listen to them.

But those on board had nonetheless managed to invoke the lighter side of their culture, their polkas, folk art, and roguish characters. Nor should they want to neglect the more serious side of their culture—their great poets and philosophers, scientists and composers. Suddenly they heard the Grundigs singing softly together Brahms' Lullaby, "*Guten Abend, gut' Nacht, von Englein bewacht . . .* "

Thus were the people who emigrated after the Great War, a smattering of personalities, a representation of mostly one stratum of society, the artisan class, among them the author's father and uncle, Theodor and Adolf Ritsche.

Max & Moritz

Moehrle farmhouse (Uncle Martin) near Eden Valley, Minnesota, with two nephews

PART THREE

"The New Country" – Fall 1923

"The German is like a willow. No matter how you bend
(uproot) him, he will always take root again."

— Alexander Solzhenitsyn

ISLAND INTERROGATION

One day soon after the passengers' final presentations, Herr Offizier Niederung tacked up a bulletin about Ellis Island. "This must mean we're getting close," Herr Seligmann observed, as the officer disappeared around the corner. The usual people were together, Theodor and Adolf, Walter, Karl Sachsen, Stefan and Michael, as well as the Grundigs, the Seligmanns, Herr Kraenke and Frau Kummer. The Stroms from Stuttgart also joined them and the Einfalts from Bavaria. They had breakfasted together and now drew near the bulletin board to read its contents. They soon learned that the items addressed disqualifications barring entry into the New Country. They skimmed through the listings apprehensively, fearing something might apply to them.[116]

They discovered, however, that the considerations did not concern anyone among the *Stammtisch* members. Nevertheless, misgivings filled them as they realized it did refer to some on board, some whom they had not gotten to know as well. The group settled on deck, choosing a spot where they could observe others without their conversation being heard. The energy they had put into their performances they now funneled into attention to all the questionable cases.

"It would be a shame," Frau Kummer moaned, hands clasping cheeks, "if someone came this far, only to be turned away at Ellis Island."

"*Genau!* Like Herr Husten," stated Frau Strom. "That cough he has is worsening by the day."

"*Richtig!* When we first boarded, I didn't even notice he had a cough." Obviously Herr Kraenke for once realized his good fortune—indeed, he had nothing on the list.

Walter said, "*Ich auch nicht.* The fellow's lungs are simply *kaputt* at this point. Probably he had something that was under control when he boarded. That or he hid it well. And despite the fact that our crossing conditions have been among the best, in an already weakened state of health, any lack of light and pure air would affect one."

Frau Kummer frowned. "*Jawohl!* Like the fumes from the furnace."

Hänschen turned to his father. "Are they saying he shouldn't have come, Vati? That it would have cleared up by itself if he had stayed home?"[117]

"*Jawohl!*" Frau Seligmann intervened. "*Der Arme!* We must pray for the poor fellow."

"I just hope he doesn't have tuberculosis." Frau Kummer shook her head and her hands fell to her middle where she twined her fingers around each other. Her fellow travelers commiserated with her statement. This time she was not exaggerating.

"We'll have to see what the authorities say," the Seligmanns said almost in unison.

"And what about Franz Blickfeld? His wife has been giving him eyedrops night and day since we boarded ship . . . " Adolf let the sentence hang.

Theodor shook his head. "It hasn't seemed to do him any good."

Stefan Lang stretched his long figure. "It's too bad they didn't catch his condition upon boarding."

"*Ja*, it sounds like the poor man is surely going to be detained." Fräulein Strom's blue eyes were distressed.

"*Ich denke schon,*" maintained Walter. "Conjunctivitis and trachoma are high on the list, especially the latter." [118]

Herr Professor Grundig said, "That's because those eye diseases are very contagious."

Michael Baumgartner scratched his head. "You can't blame America for trying to prevent an epidemic."

"Or for not wanting to add to their blind population. They figure they have enough to do, I imagine, taking care of their own blind," Walter said.

"*Ach, du lieber!*" Frau Kummer was still wringing her hands. "What if he is turned back? Think of his family."

"*Ja,* how many children does he have?" asked Matthias Seligmann. "I've seen at least five. And his wife so devoted to him, treating him twice a day."

Theodor looked down at the floor.

Adolf shifted positions. "Did you know, Theodor, that's why our sister Emilie was so concerned about that eye infection you had before we left?"

"Really?" Theodor was surprised, but thought to explain for those who might not have heard, "Our sister Emilie is a nurse."

"That's why she kept after you," continued Adolf.

Theodor appeared distressed. Her deeper motive had not occurred to him then. He thought she was just being sisterly. "Well, Franz Blickfeld is much worse. My eyes were never that bad." The Stroms noted that lately Blickfeld's eyes were discharging fiercely.

"The Blickfelds probably counted on his not getting worse. But what a shame for the family, sending the wife and the little ones back," Theodor said.

"*Ich weiß nicht,*" Walter said. "Nowadays the ship's doctors are usually very strict in checking people even before they embark, because the shipping company pays the return fare. So in this case, they might approve only his return fare."

"*Ach, du lieber!* You mean they would split up the family?" Frau Kummer was horrified.

Walter shrugged. "It happens, Frau Kummer."[119]

By this time the group was moving around the deck, all the time keeping in mind the list of reasons for rejection. "Now there's another one." All looked where Frau Kummer was focusing. Frau Kurz was leaning against the railing near the stairs. She had apparently just climbed them and had to stop to catch her breath. "If Frau Kurz gasps for air just by coming up on deck, will they let her in? She certainly can't work in that condition." Frau Kummer's voice was betraying more desperation as time went on.

Walter soothed, "I think she'll be all right, because her husband is able-bodied."

"*Gott sei Dank!*" Frau Kummer was notably relieved.

Herr Einfalt added, "*Jawohl!* That means she can rest at home when she needs it."

His wife raised her eyebrows. "In between washing, cooking, and cleaning, *meinst du?*"

"*Na ja,*" he answered.

"But Frau Kurz has also gotten worse over the Atlantic," stated the Stroms. "We didn't notice her panting at the beginning of the trip."

Walter said, "Frankly, I think the situation must be so desperate at the moment in Germany that examiners are taking more risks."

The Herr Professor Grundig said, "*Ich glaube nicht.* They had to get worse on board."

Frau Seligmann insisted, "Well, there's not too much we can do about it now. We'll just have to pray and ask the Lord to provide."

Even though they had not gotten to know them all well, it was still hard to accept that some of their compatriots might have to return to the Old Country without ever having set foot in the New Country.

Suddenly Peter Weilen came their way skipping along. The Weilen family the group had not gotten to know well, because they had kept mostly to themselves, except that Peter was always roaming about. He was displaying his usual cheerful manner, which always brightened the crowd, but this time they were all thinking about another concern.

Throughout the voyage Peter circulated items he had made out of scraps his mother found and collected in a *Bastelkasten*. From his crafts box today he was distributing butterflies. When he saw the assemblage, his cherubic face lit up. "Do you want a butterfly?" he asked everybody, his amiable manner defying his overgrown body.

"*Peterchen.* You always have something for us," Herr Seligmann said. The group was by now used to his mother's endeavors to entertain her son.

"Would you like one, Herr?"

The man responded, "*Ja!* Did you color these, *Peterchen?*"

"Yes, I did." He looked at them all shyly. "But my mom helped me." Approaching Herr Kraenke, he said, "*Guten Tag*, Herr Kraenke." They remembered how Peter had never seemed to notice Herr Kraenke's previous foul moods. In fact, Peter's manner was always so engaging that Herr Kraenke had found it hard not to respond to him. Today he even managed a smile. Thus Peter passed through the crowd, spreading not only butterflies, but also bolstering their mood. He drew the last sample from his box of crafts.

"This one's still in its cocoon, *Peterchen*," the Herr Professor Grundig observed.

"My mom said it's all right. It's just not a butterfly yet. Would you like it?"

"*Aber natürlich!*"

The boy skipped merrily on, his adolescent body reluctantly obedient to his childish whims. Frau Seligmann, almost with tears in her eyes, said, "And what's going to happen to *Peterchen?* No one would believe the joy that child brings. But he's fifteen, of age to work."

Frau Kummer shook her head in a pitiful way. "Nobody's going to employ him."

Walter shrugged. "I would hope the same is applicable to him as to Frau Kurz. Even though he may not be able to work himself, he has a family who can support him."

Frau Kummer sighed. "*Ach du lieber,* all these poor people needing medical attention."

Frau Seligmann repeated, "Let's pray about it."

Finally the group broke up, each party to go its own way. Walter fell in with the two brothers. They had come almost full circle on the deck when they saw Fräulein Fiedler, whom most would say was an attractive young woman. Others would say she was as bedecked as a Maypole. Walter surreptitiously nodded at her, as she sunned herself against the railing. "There's another one I'm concerned about."

"Fräulein Fiedler? She doesn't look sick to me." Theodor raised his brows.

Adolf lifted an eye. "Now that you mention it, she does look rather like a girl of the night." When Fräulein Fiedler was out of ear range, Walter whistled mildly. "Prostitutes are on the list all right."[120]

For the first time Theodor took a closer look. He eyed an overdone mouth and a wasp waist line, which further drew attention because her jacket was drawn tight over a buxom figure. "But why would she come here?"

"Maybe she ran out of clientele?" Walter suggested.

"But how are they going to prove anything? She hasn't misbehaved here on board."

"I'm sure they have their ways," Walter said.

He excused himself shortly, but the brothers continued strolling on deck. They had reached a more secluded part of the deck when they heard a woman crying. When Adolf asked, "*Was ist los?*" she gave a start. "Oh, I didn't hear anyone coming." She seemed extremely perturbed.

Theodor repeated, "*Also, was ist los?*"

But instead of answering what the matter was, the woman merely continued crying.

"*Na schön,*" one brother said, as each put an arm around her, murmuring, "There, there. Everything's going to be all right."

The woman shook her head violently. When she didn't volunteer any data, they asked, "*Wie heißt du noch einmal?*"

"*Ich heiße Johanna Hoffner,*" she confessed finally.

"Yes, now I remember your name. Well, Fräulein Hoffner, what makes you so sad?" She released herself from their arms and turned away. "I don't want to go to Ellis Island."

"*Entschuldigung!*" Theodor blurted. "I don't see how you can avoid that."

Theodor's attempt at excusing himself seemed to make no impression. "It's just that I don't know what's going to happen to me at Ellis Island. I don't want to be sent back," said the young lady.

"Why do you think you'll be sent back? You don't look like you have a disease." Theodor paused. "Or a criminal record?" Theodor was looking at her incredulously.

The woman shook her head to the first and almost broke out laughing at the last. But she didn't answer. The boys waited for her to go on.

"You see," she said at last, "I have no ticket to continue the journey nor anyone to meet me. I'm so afraid they'll send me back." She started crying again. "I just can't do that. I just can't go back."

"But then how did you get on board in the first place?"

"Someone was chasing me, yelling threats, so I just ran up the gangplank."

"Your husband?" Adolf suggested after a pause.

She nodded, seemingly relieved that she didn't have to explain. "I had my ticket in hand. Somehow the crew figured out the situation and, wanting to protect me, they told me to get on board. They held him back and they never returned to check the rest of my papers."

"Oh," the brothers moaned. "I don't think we have a solution for that. But you think he's going to be waiting for your return after all this time?"

To their surprise she nodded. "He will keep track of returning ships. He will be there. He told me he would."

It passed through Theodor's mind, how odd it was that someone would have that much time on hand to wait it out at the port for what seemed a lost cause to him. "It sounds as if you've had a rough time." They had noticed her before, a good-looking young woman who had a curious way of using her arms. Now they realized that the strange manner probably was neither a birth defect nor sore muscles from hard work but broken bones that had never been properly set. She again broke into sobs. Theodor returned his arm around her. "*Keine Sorge!* Something will turn up."

"That's right. Don't worry." Adolf put his arm around her other side. "But right now, you shouldn't be alone. You need to come with us. Someone will have an answer."

Gently they led her back to the crowd, not really knowing what should be their next move.

EPISODE EIGHTEEN

FOREIGN FEARS

ny day now they would see the New Country emerging on the horizon. The passengers peered constantly westward, but it seemed they would never sight the goal. Their sense of humor was reaching the breaking point. The fact that lately they left the table hungry didn't help.

As usual toward the end of a voyage, the ship's provisions were getting scarce. Besides, a mid-Atlantic storm had thrown them off course, adding on a few more days to the length of the journey. They had to content themselves with the ship's dwindling fare. Not only were items like flour and sugar running low, the porridge was getting thinner by the day, the soup no longer contained cabbage, and there were fewer carrots, potatoes, and onions.

The soup was now accompanied by hard tack, a flat, large, round, unleavened cracker made mainly from rye flour. It was kept on hand to replace bread when the galley ran out of flour. "Ship's biscuits" they were called in marine terminology. Their size and shape reminded Theodor of phonograph records he had seen in pictures. They even had a center hole, though larger than the size of a phonograph spindle. A Swedish company supplied the crisp circles strung on a pole to shipping outlets in Bremerhaven. Under normal circumstances munchers spread a portion from the large circle with butter and jam or liverwurst. But on board ship, it was usually consumed dry. The baked dough kept indefinitely if well-packaged in tins, but few found it as satisfying as a crusty piece of fresh bread with its chewy insides.

The sausage, cheese, and fresh fruit the brothers had bought in the port city hadn't lasted more than a week, since they had shared them with fellow passengers, except the oranges. The citrus fruit they had allowed no one to see. Their desire to protect themselves against scurvy was greater than others' opinions of their generosity. They figured others were probably doing the same, since from time to time they found specks of orange peel in odd places.

The morning after they had finished all the city charades, instead of maintaining a good mood, some fell to grumbling. In a crowd that was larger than their usual intimate group, one said, "Isn't this trip ever going to end?" Another said, "I can't wait until I can stretch my legs again," "Oh, for a piece of real bread!" So the complaints went.

Even Herr Kraenke regressed in attitude and took it out on those who had helped him most. Finally, when he blew up at Frau Seligmann, calling her a fanatic in a scene that even the cheerful presence of Peter Weilen could not quell, Walter took matters in hand. "Look, we can't let ourselves fall apart like this. We have to be sharp for what's coming next. We've just got to quit snarling at each other."

Herr Grundig agreed. "*Richtig!* The journey's not over."

"Of course, it's not over until we get off the boat!" retorted Herr Kraenke. "Yes, and the next step is Ellis Island."

"Ellis Island!" said Frau Kummer, hand over mouth. She had found a new cause for worry. Suddenly all the stories the passengers had heard about immigrant reception came welling up from somewhere inside, waiting to be unleashed. They all tried to talk at once.

Frau Kummer managed to speak first. "*Richtig!* I've heard immigrants are herded around like cattle, and they're fed from a wagon full of feed that the staff slaps onto their plates."

"*Ja,* the immigration officials are understaffed and overworked," said Walter, as if quoting from some book on the subject.

"That means long waits in line,"[121] Herr Kraenke replied.

"Yes," Stefan Lang agreed.

Walter countered, "Come now, even if they are true, those are minor concerns. What we really have to watch out for are dishonest money handlers, pickpockets, and inspectors." Glancing slyly at the women among them, he spoke in a more subdued tone. "Ladies will have to be aware that they may be propositioned." [122]

At this Frau Seligmann's face skewed with shock.

"*Genau!*" Herr Bischoff added. "I heard that inspectors tell a woman they'll be easy on her if she agrees to a meeting later." When someone laughed and said, "Where do they meet?" more laughter followed. With five to ten thousand milling people, solitude would be impossible.

Walter's expression remained austere, though he knew treatment of foreigners had improved since those stories. At least the crowd was now paying attention. "*Jawohl!* There are a lot of people waiting to take advantage of foreigners' ignorance."

"What else do they do?" Fräulein Strom's blue eyes showed consternation.

"Well, for example, they try to cheat foreigners who are unsure of the exchange rate."

"*Richtig!*" said Herr Strom. "Most arrivals don't know how to calculate the rate of exchange, so they just take what is handed to them."

"*Ja,*" added Walter, "Newcomers are easily deluded by shiny coins and the shiniest, the penny, is of least value."

"*Das stimmt!* My relatives cautioned us to be careful about money," said Stefan.

"*Ja,* we've heard of people ending up with as much as a seventy-five percent loss in the exchange," said Michael.

"*Ach, wie schade!* Right when people are starting out," said Frau Kummer.

"*Genau!* Then there are the officials who charge for their services," said Walter.

Theodor and Adolf maintained that their uncles' letters contained all kinds of warnings.

"*Richtig!* Relatives meeting my uncle some years ago said they had to pay a fee before they were allowed to see him," said Frau Einfalt. "Afterwards they found out that was illegal."

"In one letter my aunt wrote to me, she told us that immigration officials suggested that paying a sum would help get her through the lines more quickly," Frau Kummer said.

"That's terrible," the Frau Professor Grundig exclaimed.

"*Ja, Liebling,*" said the Herr Professor Grundig, "that's why we must be careful."

"*Aufpassen,*" interjected *Hänschen*. "Officials might accept money to put an immigrant's papers in order?"

"Like what?" asked Theodor, thinking of Fräulein Hoffner.

"Well, to overlook questionable legal or medical conditions," said the Frau Professor.

"Or to forge papers," said her husband.

"Immigrants can be detained, quarantined, and even sent back," said Walter to the larger audience.

The shudder that went through a Blickfeld boy, who was walking past them, was hard to miss. Johanna Hoffnung, also there, turned away. However, Theodor began to think, since they hadn't yet solved her problem, that's one way for her to get through the gates.

"That all sounds to me like a lot of bribery," said Frau Seligmann flatly.

Just then Offizier Niederung came along to hand out inspection cards. "What's that I heard about bribery? You're intending to bribe me?"

They laughed, then explained their topic of conversation. At the end of their enumeration they asked, "*Ist das alles richtig, Herr Offizier?*"

"*Kann sein.* It always pays to be careful," the crewman said. "But I think you people are telling each other stories you've heard from previous immigrants, *nicht wahr?*"

The passengers nodded weakly.

"Well, it's true, conditions were at one time pretty miserable, but that was back in the late 1800s. Let me tell you a little of the history. Just after the turn of the century, conditions got considerably better when the current president, Theodore Roosevelt, got wind of what was going on. He made a surprise visit to the immigration facilities at Ellis Island to see if rumors he'd heard were true. Well, he was horrified at the treatment of foreigners and the conditions for sanitation. The upshot of it was he fired the current contractors in areas like food and baggage and money changing, and issued the jobs to more reliable companies. Later a man named La Guardia[123] further improved the lot for immigrants. Of course," he added, "the '*Litzers*'[124] are still with us."

"*Litzers?*" repeated Herr Kraenke.

"*Ja*, 'scalpers.' Those who take advantage of passengers who don't know the ropes and besides are too tired to think after the exhausting transatlantic crossing. Those persons think they can't make an honest living. *Aber keine Sorge!* I have a bag full of American coins I'll show you, so you can get used to their value."

Everyone seemed relieved until the Herr Offizier Niederung said, "I think these days, however, that your biggest problem will come after you get through Ellis Island."

Frau Kummer's face returned to a look of apprehension. "What do you mean?"

"I'm talking about xenophobia."

"Zeno-what? What's that?" Herr Einfalt wondered.

"That's fear of foreigners."

Stefan and Michael suddenly broke out in laughter. "But why would they have fear of foreigners, when most came from foreigners?" asked Stefan.

"That's where we're all going, to relatives who came earlier," stated Michael.

"*Richtig!* They forget their ancestors were at one time also foreign," said Walter.

"Well then, what are they afraid of?" asked Fräulein Strom.

"That you'll take their jobs," said the Herr Offizier.

"Oh-h," the crowd murmured, suddenly serious.

The Herr Offizier Niederung continued. "*Ja*, conditions have gotten so bad that for the first time two years ago, Congress enacted quotas."[125]

"Quotas?" asked Herr Einfalt.

"*Ja*, it's stipulated how many of each nationality is allowed to enter." But the Herr Offizier Niederung had to move on to complete his tasks. "I'll bring you the coins."

Frau Kummer threw up her hands in a gesture of giving up. "It's all so confusing."

"All I know," said Herr Kraenke, "is that I'll be glad to get off this boat and stretch my legs." It was obvious his even mood was likewise being stretched.

With that, the group parted ways. Walter said as he headed in the same direction as the two brothers, "I think I know what your biggest problem at Ellis Island will be."

"Why are you looking at us like that?" Theodor asked, with a sidewise look of mirth at Adolf.

"Because some of us will have to pay good attention unless we don't mind getting the spelling of our last names changed."[126]

"Aha," said Theodor. "Adolf, we'll have to practice spelling our last name in English."

"*Jawohl!*" said Adolf. "Sounds like it."

Later, many with equally difficult surnames, caught on to the idea. While some mulled over the Herr Offizier Niederung's coins, others could be heard sounding out the letters of their names in English. Every so often Walter or Karl Sachsen gave them extra help. "Ar," they kept saying to the brothers, "not 'air,' that's German. 'I' as in the month of 'Mai' or English 'my,' and 'T' like when the English have 'tea.'" Next came: "S is 's.'"

"*Gott sei Dank!* We have a letter that sounds the same," said Theodor.

"Close enough at least. Now comes 'C.' It rhymes with 'tea.'"

They both tried it. "*Ja,* but without the 'tsetse' sound for the 'c'. Just an 's' sound," Walter cautioned.

"'H' sounds the same as in your surname 'tsch,' but with an 'ä' before it.

"The last 'E' rhymes again with 'tea.'"

So they practiced R-I-T-S-C-H-E until Walter made a further suggestion. "You know what you need to do?" Theodor and Adolf looked at each other shrugging. "Pause before and after the 'S,'" The two shrugged again. "The 's' otherwise is likely to be left out," insisted

Theodor Ritsche

Walter. "I have a friend whose last name is Fritsche and that's what he does to get it right."

So they went about the deck saying R-I-T-(pause five seconds) S-(pause five seconds) C-H-E, and again R-I-T-*(eins, zwei, drei, vier, fünf)* S-*(eins, zwei, drei, vier, fünf)* C-H-E. and again R-I-T- (one, two, three, four, five) S-(one, two, three, four, five) C-H-E. Soon others picked up on it and started marching to the rhythm.

When Walter and Karl Sachsen observed them, they said, "*Großartig!* Only don't say the numbers. Just think them."

That night, Theodor said to his brother, "*Na ja*, Adolf, we may have left an impossible situation *im Alten Land*, but this next step *im Neuen Land* might be just as challenging, if even spelling is going to be all this trouble."

Adolf sighed, "*Na ja*, what else will we have to learn?"

EPISODE NINETEEN

MISS LIB

The next day, Theodor, who had been looking westward into the distance, suddenly said, "Look! Is that land I see?" All rushed to gaze in that direction. *Gewiß!* There was a shadow along the horizon.

Some time later, Herr Strom said, "What's that object poking up above the horizon?"

"It's probably the Statue of Liberty," said Michael.

"Or a skyscraper," said Stefan.

The soon-to-be immigrants watched, still and silent, as the horizon came into better focus. Then *Hänschen* said, "That is the Statue of Liberty! See that arm raised among the tall buildings?" The young people started jumping around. Soon their spry elders did likewise. Even the oldsters, who had spent the last few days seemingly drained of energy, came back to life, clapping their hands and stamping their feet.

After they had come yet closer, a hush fell over the crowd as persons fell to contemplating their private dreams. What did Miss Lib mean to them? America was the chance to practice one's trade and make a decent living doing it. As long as they worked hard, they believed they would find economic success. For some the officer's quotes ran through their minds as well: "Give me your huddled masses yearning to breathe free."[127] Theodor was thinking how difficult it had been to keep his hands unoccupied on crossing the Atlantic. They were itching to feel the heft of a hammer, the vibrations of sawing a plank, the flicks of the wrist carving a block of wood into a meaningful figure—indeed, to feel the satisfaction of accomplishing a project. He wondered, did Adolf feel the same about electricity? He doubted that it could capture the imagination the way wood did.

The Herr Offizier Niederung had reminded them of the lady's story, how some Frenchmen conceived the idea as they sat together pondering their own fight for freedom and admiring at the same time the American notion of "*la liberté*." The statue was supposed to be a gift from the people of France to the people of America to commemorate its first centennial in 1876, but it was late in coming.[128]

Someone suddenly shouted, rousing them from their dream. "I do believe *das Fräulein Freiheit* smiles at us." "*Jawohl!*" They were now close enough to see the lady's features.

"So she does," said another. "That must be a sign of good luck!"

"*Ja*, maybe better in this case than finding a horseshoe or a four-leaf clover." "Or even a ladybug or a piglet."

"Or a lucky mushroom."

"Wait! They probably don't have the same good luck symbols as in the Old Country."

Frau Seligmann responded, "I think we should be thankful that we all have arrived in the New Country safe and sound."

"Amen!" said the crowd.

It was now turning dark, and the lady's crown cast a soft light into the dusk, the light of her torch reflecting in the water.

Walter mused, "Miss Lib has occupied her island going on forty years now."

"*Wirklich!*"

Just then they were startled by a severe jolt. It knocked some unsteady people to the floor. Frau Kummer cried out, "*Um Gottes willen!* What next?" But the children started giggling. Some of them had fallen as well, and it inspired them to roll around gleefully on the deck. Soon the passengers realized that the *Hannover* had merely bumped against the dock. They shouted excitedly, as if the significance of the feat were just sinking in. "*Wir haben es geschafft.*" "We made it!" They ran around hugging each other. "*Wir sind heil und gesund angekommen.*" "We got here safe and sound! *Es ist ein Wunder!* It's a miracle!" They formed a circle, joined hands, dancing around as they shouted their thankful statements. "*Glückspilze sind wir!*"

"Lucky mushrooms!" murmured Walter to himself, grinning.

After a moment it occurred to them to ask, "But where is the immigration building?" They had seen nothing that looked like the picture, which the Herr Offizier had shown them, a red-brick-and-cream building with stone-framed arches. Then they noticed people on the dock.

"We're unloading," someone said, but the Herr Offizier Niederung said hastily. "*Leider nicht für Sie!* Just stay put. Those are first- and second-class passengers disembarking from another ship."

"What do you mean, unfortunately not for us? You mean we steerage passengers can't get off yet?" piped up Herr Kraenke.

"*Richtig.* We'll be taking you to the ferry dock, which will take you to Ellis Island."

"Oh, so we'll be off the ship soon."

"It takes a while. We'll go through a maze of channels to get there."

When the Herr Offizier Niederung had gone, Walter commented, "*Leider!* Only the poor go through Ellis Island, and the poor have time."[129]

"Well, we'll see how long that lasts!" the more stubborn aboard said.

It was a challenge to make their fortune in the New Country and to return to the Old Country by first- or, at least, second-class ticket.

After the ship arrived at the ferry dock, the usual lukewarm soup of the last few days, with potatoes and a bit of stringy beef awaited them. Suppertime over, there was still no ferry. They settled down to wait. Soon thereafter the dark of night came upon them. A passenger spoke out as they resumed their place on deck, "*Um Gottes willen!* I wish we could have made this journey in daylight, so we could have seen more."

"Not me," said Adolf, watching on deck the panorama of electric bulbs light up one by one on shore. He had never seen so much electrical power in one spot. Yes, indeed, here he would find work. Watching Adolf, Theodor thought—maybe electricity does have its own attraction.

The sight of a ferry heading their way excited the voyagers. But a passing officer said, "That's not for you. See that ship with the British flag? It's next in line." The officer shook his head. "I would expect you'll sleep on board tonight. It's late and I doubt there will be any more ferries tonight."

The next day they thought surely they would be first in line. Ferries indeed came, but not for them. It was always for someone else's ship. The delay left them restless. The Herr Offizier Niederung explained that there was no place to house them, therefore they had to remain on board their ship.

On deck the brothers finally saw an opportunity to help Fräulein Hoffner. Walter was in the crowd and the Grundigs and Jakob Friedman, people who,—in short—might know what to do.

Theodor, realizing there was not much time left, suddenly broke into the general conversation. "Do all of you have American sponsors?"

"*Aber natürlich!*" snapped Mr. Kraenke, who was inordinately impatient today. "You can't get in anymore without them. The immigration laws have become so strict."

Unknowingly the gruff, regressive statement led right to the topic that had been weighing on their minds. "Actually we have someone with us who's gotten this far without papers," Adolf said.

"Who?" the crowd murmured unbelievingly. "*Das ist ja Wahnsinn.*"

"Foolish or not, it has happened to Fräulein Hoffner." Adolf nodded to her, now at his side.

Frau Kummer looked at her, gasping. "*Ach du lieber,* what are you going to do, *Fräulein?*"

"*Ich—ich weiß es nicht!*" Her stammering voice and shaking hands betrayed her fright.

"We bring it up because we thought maybe someone had an idea," said Adolf.

Frau Kummer moved closer. "*Ach, liebes Fräulein Hoffner,* you have no ticket? And nobody's coming to meet you? *Ach,* what are you going to do?" She put her hands to her mouth.

Walter stepped in. "Actually, even though the laws are much stricter than years back, other customs have relaxed. One of them is the increased number of ethnic and religious agencies. I understand representatives are usually present at Ellis Island."

"If that doesn't work," said the Herr Professor Grundig, "there are the Red Cross, the YMCA, and the Salvation Army, all looking to help people regardless of religion or nationality."

"But what about papers?" Fräulein Hoffner looked ready to break down again.

Walter said, "*Nein, nein,* Fräulein Hoffner, surely some agency will help. They take responsibility for bereft immigrants by guaranteeing the government that unfortunates won't become public charges. They provide temporary support until immigrants can get on their feet."

"And you think they will help me?" Fräulein Hoffner said incredulously.

"I wouldn't worry," Walter said. "These organizations are used to such things. Lots of people have such problems."

"They do?" She cast him an unbelieving look. It just didn't fit with the Wilhelminian bureaucracy to which she was accustomed.

Walter nodded. "Furthermore, I think they'll believe you. You look pretty honest."

Fräulein Hoffner smiled, as a feeling of gratitude swept over her. "*Gott sei Dank!*"

"Yes, God be thanked." Frau Kummer sighed.

"But I wouldn't reveal everything at first," Walter cautioned. "Just tell them that those who were supposed to meet you didn't come. They may not even ask for evidence of papers."

"*Ach, danke schön, danke schön!*"

"But if they ask, then is the time to tell them the true story."

Jakob Friedman suddenly stepped forward. "If you want, I can accompany you, Fräulein Hoffner, until we find someone who can help."

"*Sehen Sie? Sie haben Glück!*" Adolf nodded in approval.

"Yes," Theodor agreed, "you're lucky. It's going to work out. After all, it isn't as if you deliberately tried to be dishonest."

The crowd quickly hushed for the approach of the Herr Offizier, looking fresh and alert in a starched uniform by comparison with the rumpled clothing of the immigrants. He was coming around again. "*Inspektion,*" he announced. "*Inspektion.*"

"Inspection?" The word hummed through the crowd, followed by

Form 2303
U. S. DEPARTMENT OF LABOR
NATURALIZATION SERVICE

TRIPLICATE
[To be given to the person making the Declaration.]

No. __957__

UNITED STATES OF AMERICA

DECLARATION OF INTENTION

☞ **Invalid for all purposes seven years after the date hereof**

State of __Minnesota__
County of __Stearns__ } *ss:*

In the __District__ Court
of __Seventh Judicial District__

I, __Theodor Ritsche__ , aged __19__ years,
occupation __Carpenter__ , do declare on oath that my personal
description is: Color __white__, complexion __fair__ , height __5__ feet __7__ inches,
weight __130__ pounds, color of hair __brown__ , color of eyes __brown__
other visible distinctive marks __not any__
I was born in __Daisendorf, Germany__
on the __18__ day of __November__ , anno Domini 1 __903__ ; I now reside
at __Eden Valley, Stearns Co. Minn.__
(Give number, street, city or town, and State.)
I emigrated to the United States of America from __Bremen, Germany__
on the vessel __Hanover, North German Lloyds Line__ ; my last
(If the alien arrived otherwise than by vessel, the character of conveyance or name of transportation company should be given)
foreign residence was __Daisendorf, Germany__ ; I am __not__ married; the name
of my { wife / husband } is ----------------------; { she / he } was born at ----------------------
and now resides at --
It is my bona fide intention to renounce forever all allegiance and fidelity to any foreign
prince, potentate, state, or sovereignty, and particularly to ....
.... __The German Empire__ , of whom I am now a subject;
I arrived at the port of __New York__ , in the
State of __New York__ , on or about the __23d__ day
of __September__ , anno Domini 1 __923__ ; I am not an anarchist; I am not a
polygamist nor a believer in the practice of polygamy; and it is my intention in good faith
to become a citizen of the United States of America and to permanently reside therein:
SO HELP ME GOD

__Theodor R. Ritsche__
(Original signature of declarant)

[SEAL]

Subscribed and sworn to before me in the office of the Clerk of
said Court this __2nd__ day of __July__ , anno Domini 192 __4__

__John L. Somunich__
Clerk of the __District__ Court.

By __Charles Schmel__ , __Deputy__ Clerk.

16—1170

"*Wat iss dat?*"

"*Ja, wat iss dat?*" mimicked the Herr Offizier Niederung, laughing. Then he returned to High German. "*Das ist eine Inspektionskarte.*" He raised high a card. The sight horrified the crowd for a minute. "*Ruhig,*" he assured them. "There's nothing negative here." Soon they calmed down so he could continue. "Filling out these inspection cards all together will help your information to be more accurate," he informed them. "I'll go through the information with you right now line by line. The first you recognize. Name is '*Name.*' First your *Nachname,* then your *Vorname.*" He proceeded slowly through the items, pausing after each, so the passengers would have time to write. Soon they had all filled in: Point of Origin—Bremerhaven; Name of Ship—Hannover; Point of Arrival: New York. "For date of arrival," continued the Herr Offizier, "you're going to put today's date— September 23, 1923."

The Herr Offizier concluded, "Furthermore, this means you'll be getting off the boat today, so get your belongings together."

It was not long before their dilapidated, makeshift baggage appeared on deck as it had when they had boarded, but this time without salami and bread protruding atop packages.

The Herr Offizier Niederung continued. "*Hände hoch!*"

The passengers felt relaxed enough to laugh. "Is this a hold-up?" asked Herr Einfalt.

Offizier Niederung laughed back. "I mean, hands up with your railroad tickets in your hands."

"Railroad tickets, when we haven't gone though Ellis Island yet?" Herr Kraenke's rough voice rumbled through the crowd. "Isn't that a little soon?"

"With all the other papers you'll get, I don't want you to mislay your railroad ticket, Herr Kraenke." The officer proceeded among the passengers, pinning their tickets to the lapels of those who already had them. Some, including the two brothers, still needed to purchase them.

Then the officer chuckled. "Now I have something for you." He smiled as he produced a map of the United States. "*Sehen Sie?* You can see where you're all going."

Soon the immigrants were looking up the location of their final destinations and where they would be in relation to others on board. Someone found a pencil, and one after another the passengers proceeded to mark their destinations on the map. When they were finished, they found not only unlanded farmers who were joining relatives in the central middle states, the breadbasket of America, but also woodworkers going to the forests in Washington state and North Carolina, steelworkers going to Pennsylvania, factory workers to Michigan. The Grundigs were going to St. Louis, where the Herr Professor would again practice his profession. The two brothers marked Minneapolis on the map.

Not long thereafter, the Herr Offizier Niederung told them it was time to get in line to get on the ferry. As they boarded, the officer shouted, "*Kopf hoch!*"

"*Gewiß!* Chin up!" repeated Walter, as he turned around. "*Kameraden*, this is the last we'll see of Herr Offizier Niederung. "Let's give him a *dreimal hoch!*"

On their last bath day Adolf had noted that Theodor's ribs and kneecaps were showing more than ever. He was no longer just slender but downright gaunt. Adolf mentioned the fact merely in passing to the Herr Offizier Niederung. The very next day the officer came with a package in one hand and a napkin covering an object in the other. He led Theodor to privacy. "We've got to take care of you, Theodor," he vowed. Inside the package were butter cookies and under the napkin a cup of strong hot tea with generous amounts of sugar and canned milk. "*Es geht bald los,*" the crewman said clandestinely. "*Keine Sorge!* Soon it'll be over, and you'll be on a good diet." The next time he came with a plate of noodles drenched in beef gravy. He supplied Theodor several more times with extra rations. They never learned the source. It didn't matter. Adolf noticed immediate improvement in his brother's condition.

The immigrants saluted the officer who had befriended them so nicely three times, raising their arms as if they held *Biersteine*. Then as if still holding beer mugs, they marched down the gangplank. Theodor and Adolf stayed close to each other. Their brother in Argentina suddenly popped into Theodor's head. "I wonder if our brother Karl felt like this when he landed in Buenos Aires," Theodor whispered to Adolf.

"Oh," said Adolf, "that colorful Bohemian quarter called 'La Boca,' the mouth. Did you picture a big mouth swallowing the hordes of immigrants?" They looked at each other and laughed. Strange the thoughts that came into one's head at such moments. Then Theodor said gravely, "The three of us, we learned our trades according to Old World tradition, but our homeland has no place for us to practice them. So on to the New World!"

UP TO THE GREAT HALL AND
DOWN THE STAIRCASE OF SEPARATION

When the ferry left them off, the *Hannover* passengers with less luggage helped those with more luggage as well as with their children and their elderly. A shout went up as they realized that, at last, after more than a month, they were again on *terra firma*.

As they crossed the walkway to the stairs, someone joked, "If your name means anything to you, make sure it's spelled correctly." "You don't want to enter with one name and come out with another!" joked someone else. Another added, "*Jawohl!* Because later it'll cost you to get it corrected."

Then admonitions about money proceeded fast and furiously. "Watch your wallets" . . . "And your pockets!" . . . "Count your money!" . . . "Do your math!" . . . "*Ja,* take time to figure out the Mark's worth!"

Mounting the stairs to the Registry Room, or what was usually called the Great Hall, they looked up to see the railing lined with people, their eyes riveted on them. Why so many curiosity-seekers? Didn't they see new arrivals everyday?[130]

When they commented to Walter, a note of irony reflected in his eyes. "That's not it, sorry to say. They are examiners and that ascent is often referred to as the 'six-second medical exam.'"

The Herr Professor Grundig raised his eyebrows. Walter confirmed, from his previous journey, "Yes, immigrants as they come up the stairs are being observed for physical debilities such as limping, shortness of breath, back problems, or anything else that might hinder their ability to work."

"Really?" said Frau Kummer, as the rest recoiled for a moment at the thought, pondering whether they had exhibited their best walk.

"*Ja,* you must be able to work," taunted Theodor. "Yet it's illegal to have a job lined up, *nicht wahr?*"[131]

"Yes, it has to do with taking work away from a citizen," declared Walter.

At the top of the steps they showed their passports to examiners, who inspected throat, hands, and skin. Last, their hair was riffled through with fine combs. Then the passengers were led to long rows of benches to wait for their remaining tests.

Walter had a chance to whisper to his colleagues, "*Ausgezeichnet,* nobody got an 'Sc.'"

"An excellent for what? What does 'Sc' mean?"[132]

"'Sc' is an abbreviation for the English word 'scalp.' They were looking for lice, or worse, for the dreaded scalp disease called favus."

"They're deported for that, *richtig?*" asked Frau Kummer, to which Walter nodded.

The wait seemed interminable, especially after having spent so much time already in the harbor. As they had been told, the workers looked understaffed and overworked. In the Great Hall, crowds of people waited unattended, their baggage strewn apart probably because they were looking in it for something to engage them during the wait. Clerks flew by hastily with apparently urgent errands, and examiners looked haggard as if prodding themselves to quicken the pace.

When Walter saw his companions getting restless, he said, "When they ask for your name, that's a test, too, you know!"

"For what? We know who we are," said Herr Kraenke.

"They ask simple questions to judge whether you can hear and speak properly."

"Oh!" the immigrants murmured, relieved.

But Frau Kummer needed to know more. "How do you say '*Wie*

heißen Sie' in English?"

"Keine Sorge!" Walter assured her, "that much officials can say in German." As they walked further, Walter said, "There used to be in this whole area wire-enmeshed stanchions where immigrants stood in line. For small children the time was too long. There was much more crying to endure. And it seemed there were always innumerable persons ahead. There were other points of entry, but ninety percent of America's immigrants came through Ellis Island in the early 1900s and something like five thousand to ten thousand immigrants a day passed through their gates."

"That's when our sponsors came. It's no wonder they complained about conditions,"[133] said the brothers. Others nodded as if they knew to what the brothers were referring.

Finally the conversation quieted down, as weariness overcame the travelers. Children settled into a game of marbles, mothers read to little children, fathers took older children for walks.

At last a guard announced, *"Pässe, bitte!* Have your passports ready, please."

Someone announced, after finding a clock, that they had already been there two hours.

They were led to a room of men in white coats. Doors behind them periodically opened, revealing inner chambers. *"Um Gottes willen!* Did you see all those bottles behind those doors?" cried Frau Kummer.

Walter explained, *"Ja,* they're probably cleaning agents of sorts, shampoos for delousing and rubbing alcohol for disinfecting." He shrugged. "More thorough examinations will also be directed there."

"And then what happens?" Frau Kummer asked.

"That depends. If they can quickly disinfect something, then they can go. If they have a temporary illness like a childhood disease or a case of pneumonia, they'll be put in a hospital ward until they get well enough to continue their journey. But if the examiners determine that a candidate has something like favus or that the breadwinner's back won't allow him to work or that someone's eyes are only going to get weaker, they'll make arrangements for them to return to the Old

Country. That's when they go down the staircase of separation, to the section that leads back to the harbor."

"*Um Gottes willen,*" said Frau Kummer. But she didn't have long to fret, for the lines were going quickly now, two to three minutes per person. They watched their fellow passengers as doctors flipped eyelids with fingers or hairpins, to examine for trachoma. From time to time an inspector chalked some letters on a passenger's lapel. The rest of them were trying to figure out what the initials meant.

Their little group watched anxiously as the *Hannover* passengers they were most concerned about preceded them in the line. Poor Herr Husten couldn't even control his coughing long enough to get past the examiner. The doctor merely shook his head and chalked a letter on his lapel. He never even looked at the rest of the family. When the coughing man turned slightly, the onlookers saw a giant P on his coat lapel.

They watched as down the line the family was shunted in a different direction from the rest. The group was dismayed. Finally, Frau Kummer said, "*Ich verstehe nicht.* 'P?' Wouldn't it be 'L,' I thought the word for lungs was much the same as the German '*Lungen*'."

"It's 'P' for pulmonary," explained Walter. "He probably has tuberculosis."

Soon the Blickfeld family's turn came, and the whole group set their eyes on them. Franz Blickfeld stood behind his family, so the doctor checked first the children, then the mother. When he came to the father, he shook his head and gave a sign of hopelessness, as if to convey he had checked the family in vain. He chalked some initials on his lapel. Soon the whole family was directed the same way as the Hustens.

"What did the letters say?" . . . "CT" . . . "Why doesn't it say 'E' for eyes?" . . . "What could 'CT' mean?"

Finally Walter ventured, "It's probably an abbreviation for Conjunctivitus-Trachoma. That means an eye doctor will diagnose his case more thoroughly. General eye trouble, which includes poor eyesight I would think would be indicated with an 'E', but 'CT' . . . well, we were all worried about him. And now that they've disappeared,

I doubt we'll see them again. Like we said, they are two of the most common reasons for deportation."

The information went down the line of *Hannover's* passengers with much whispering among themselves. At last Frau Kummer summarized, "*Um Gottes willen!* We didn't even have a chance to say good-bye."

The thought shook them for a minute. At last Theodor said, "I hope whatever happens, that the family can at least stay together. The members all seemed so devoted to each other. Things might get worse if they are separated."

Again there wasn't long to think about the Blickfelds. They were all thinking—*Gott sei Dank* as they saw Frau Kurz waved through with the rest of her family. Walter said, "That confirms what I thought, since she's not considered the primary breadwinner, she's waved on."

"*Jawohl!*" said Herr Seligmann. "As has been already said, she can stay at home and rest."

"Yes," droned his wife for the second time, "in between cooking, cleaning, washing, and ironing."

In a moment the Weilen family's turn came. They felt more relaxed watching *Peterchen*, yet when he also was waved on, Frau Kummer couldn't resist a *Gott sei Dank!*

Behind him Stefan nudged Theodor's arm. "They called your name."

"*Ach so!*" He didn't recognize it from the pronunciation. He looked around for Adolf, but he was already in the group waiting for their legal exam. How did they get split up? Theodor had been counting on Adolf's help. Well, now he would really have to concentrate. He began repeating to himself, R-I-T—S—C-H-E, R-I-T—S—C-H-E, and don't say the numbers in between.

Still the interview did not go well despite his practicing. The inspector took a look at Theodor's card and asked, "What's your middle name?"

Middle name, middle name went through Theodor's brain. What could that be? Finally he said, "*Ich weiß nicht.*"

Unfortunately for Theodor the examiner knew that German phrase and exclaimed, "What? You don't know your middle name?"

Theodor grew flustered. He could see from the missing blank that something went there. But he thought to himself—I have only two names. People here have three names?

Luckily a German interpreter came along. "In some areas of Germany it's not customary to have middle names." Then he was gone to help someone else.

Theodor thought—I think I'm in trouble.

The examiner shrugged. "Okay, let's go on. So, your last name is written last here. How do you spell that? I can't read this writing." Theodor tried out his spelling, but evidently even after all the practice, his letters were still not clear enough. The inspector wrote down R-I-T-C-H-I-E. Theodor looked at the block print and insisted, "*Nein, nein.*"

Soon the examiner was waving his arms wildly, mumbling something Theodor couldn't understand. The interpreter approached again. "What seems to be the problem?"

"I just can't make anything out of this fractured German."

"Not fractured, *Fraktur,*" the interpreter explained patiently. "That's the name of their writing." He took the form Theodor had filled out and spelled for the examiner: R-I-T—S—C-H-E, just like Theodor had practiced. He smiled. He wasn't going to lose his surname. As the interpreter departed, Theodor too, began moving away. "Not so fast, young man," said the examiner, uttering something in a commanding tone.

This time Walter came from behind to the rescue. "*Setz deinen Friedrich Wilhelm darunter.*" He pointed to where Theodor's 'John Henry' should go. After Theodor had signed his name, he rushed to join his brother. Adolf told him indignantly, "I had to fight to keep the 's' in our last name!"

"*Ja, ich auch.* It's a good thing we were prepared," said Theodor who then kept his silence.

Frau Seligmann exclaimed. "*Sehen Sie mal!* Fräulein Fiedler's turn has come." Was she going to get a mark? The inspector took one look at her brightly rouged cheeks, her darkened eyes, her expanded lips. It didn't take long for the inspector to chalk her jacket lapel. The whispers began at the back of the group. "What does it say?" . . . "I don't know"

. . . "I can't read it, it's too small." By the time the whispers got to the front, the made-up young miss had turned toward them to snatch up her baggage. "What did you see? . . . Was it an X?" They knew that meant suspicion of mental disease. "No, actually there are two letters." Finally those in front passed the mark down the line. "It says . . . 'SI.' What does that mean?"

Walter quickly volunteered. "It means Special Inquiry. In German something like *Sonderinterrogation*, which probably means that our suspicions about Fräulein Fiedler were right." Sure enough, she too disappeared behind a closed door.

"*Ach*," said Frau Kummer, "it's too bad someone didn't advise her to tone down her make-up." The Seligmanns stared at her, incredulous.

But there wasn't much time to ponder. They were being led to the legal exam room. Walter was reminded of another story. "There has been much legal reform on the part of many. But I want to mention a story by La Guardia. He insisted that too often examiners were misdiagnosing the intelligence of foreigners, because they were testing culture not intelligence."

"They used to have the immigrants, those who didn't understand English, interpret pictures. In one instance, a Czech was asked to explain the picture of a dead rabbit next to a hole. Well, of course, where he came from food was scarce and hunting was encouraged, so his version related that they had just killed the rabbit and were going to cook it for dinner. But the expected answer was they were going to bury it."

"So he failed the test!"

Walter said, "*Jawohl!*"

After the legal exam the *Hannover* passengers joined others already waiting. "The big ordeal is over," Walter said, sighing for them all. "Now it's a matter of deciding which way to go down the stairs. To the left you catch the ferry to Lower Manhattan to enter New York City. To the right means connecting with the New Jersey Railroad."

"Then what is in the middle?" inquired little Hans Grundig.

"Well, *Hänschen*, the detained people go there. That's why these steps are called the Staircase of Separation."

Suddenly they saw Johanna Hoffner coming toward them with Jakob Friedman and Karl Sachsen trailing not far behind. Before they even reached the group, Johanna cried. "I'm so glad you're still here. I wanted to say *Auf Wiedersehen!*"

Frau Kummer gasped. "You're all taken care of then?"

"*Ja,* Jakob took me to the Hebrew Immigrant Aid Society. They will take care of me until I find work and also help me get the proper papers."

"*Siehst du?* That is really luck! *Du bist wirklich ein Glückspilz.*" The brothers beamed.

Frau Kummer reluctantly admitted, "Yes, you really are a lucky mushroom." They went around hugging their good-byes. The group watched Jakob and Johanna, in tow, as they turned, arm in arm, with Karl Sachsen following closely behind toward the Manhattan ferry.

After a sigh of relief, Frau Strom suggested they bow their heads a moment that all go well with the Hustens and the Blickfeld family as well as with Fräulein Fiedler. The Seligmanns looked around at all the bowed heads before they acquiesced.

When they were finished, Walter said, "I guess you can see now why Ellis Island is called simultaneously 'Island of Hope, Island of Tears.'"

ON A SIDEWALK OF NEW YORK

Those remaining spent a moment in reverie. At last Frau Kummer broke the silence. "Well, some of us still have to get our railroad tickets. I hope they still have something for today." She turned to the staircase that led to the New Jersey train station.

As they walked, Walter said, "My relatives used to tell the story that in America the streets are paved with gold."

Many nodded, for the phrase was also familiar to them.

Walter continued, "Did they also say they learned upon arrival that not only are they not paved with gold, on the contrary, many roads are not paved at all?"

Michael offered, "I think we'll find that out where we're going, *nicht wahr*, Theodor and Adolf?"

"*Sicher* in the Midwest. Furthermore, I understand the immigrant is expected to pave them," added Theodor. They laughed at the old saying.

Michael said, "*Ja*, we have our work cut out for us."

They had reached the staircase when Adolf suddenly paused. "Shouldn't we wait for Stefan? He doesn't have his ticket yet and will want to be with us on the train west."

"*Eine gute Idee!*" said Walter. "Otherwise, do we have everybody?" He looked around. Some of the others had already veered to the Manhattan exit. The bachelors, Stefan, Michael, Theodor, and Adolf, had refrained from wandering off. The Grundig family was taking advantage of the lull to read signs in English with *Hänschen*. Walter surveyed the rest carefully once more. Even those continuing to the

East Coast were there. "I don't see anyone missing," he said to those around. Then he collared the rest of the New Jersey people and said, "Let's wait down the stairs for Stefan, because here we're in the way."

"Where is Stefan anyway?" Frau Kummer inquired noisily.

"He had to go to the room where the Kaiser goes alone." The others nodded. "But we have some time before our train leaves."

"We could get our tickets." Frau Kummer's tone was urgent, as if movement bid her on.

"I think we should wait," said Walter. "Or Stefan might not get on the same train."

When they reached the sidewalk, Theodor paused a moment to span the panorama. Taking in a big breath, he let it out slowly. His eyes had a far-off look as if he saw something visionary in all the iron, steel, glass, and concrete. Finally his mouth opened. "Now that we're here in this grand city, I wish we had some time to see it."

Walter teased, "What do you want? You just saw Ellis Island and the Statue of Liberty."

Theodor didn't pause to think. "Actually, I would like to see the Roebling Bridge."

Walter shook his head. "I've never heard of it. Are you sure it's in New York?"

"*Doch!*" said Theodor, his chest expanding. "The bridge is hailed as the Eighth Wonder of the World."

"America has such a distinction?" Frau Kummer's face betrayed doubt.

"*Jawohl!* And I'd like to see it because it's new." His stance revealed modified defiance.

"How old is it?" demanded Herr Kraenke.

Theodor shrugged. "In age it's only about forty years." Knowing that in European terms that would be scant time, he hurried on before any-one could scoff. "I was talking about its new type of construction. It's a suspension bridge."[134]

"*Genau, eine Hängebrücke.* I did hear about that," said Walter. "How do you know all these things?"

"I read books about such things and how they're constructed."

"*Stimmt's*, now I know!" Walter struck a hand to his forehead. "You mean the Brooklyn Bridge! The one that connects Brooklyn with Manhattan."

"Here it's called the Brooklyn Bridge?" Theodor couldn't avoid a tone of disappointment, which provoked in him a momentary silence.

Walter nodded. "I remember reading when it opened, it cost a penny to cross it."

"Hm-m! I wonder how much it costs now," Adolf said.

"*Ich weiß nicht!* I do know it's more than a penny. But Theodor, when we were in the harbor, we could see the bridge in the distance."

"*Ja,* I wondered about that," Theodor said, recovering from his disillusion. "In that case I think I did see it. So I guess that will have to do for now. But listen here! Roebling's ideas are important because he helped others to look at design in a different light."

Herr Strom said, "The man must have been proud of his accomplishment."

"Actually, Roebling was killed on the job, so he never saw the finished bridge."

"*Wie schade!*" said Frau Strom.

"You know," chimed in the Herr Professor, "I read something on Roebling. It was in a series of articles about people who found the Old Country had become too small. Roebling, for instance, was an inventor, but he never accomplished anything marketable until he got to the New Country."

"*Richtig,* Herr Professor. And getting back to what might be called marketing strategies, according to the book I read, many German inventions were never brought to fruition in Europe," said Theodor.

"*Ja,* that's true," said the Herr Professor. "And not only of Germans, but of other Europeans. Lots of inventions, though conceived by Europeans, were first launched on the American market. Many even had improved designs."

"That's it," said Theodor, excited that the listeners were catching the drift. "As I see it, America, having little history of craftsmanship, at least as we know it in Europe, had a clean slate on which to build their ideas about production."

The Herr Professor Grundig affirmed, "I know what you mean, Theodor. You're talking about the guilds that developed the training sequence—*Lehrling, Geselle, Meister.*"

"*Ja,*" agreed Michael, "apprentice, journeyman, master craftsman."

"The New World in a way simply scrapped the entrenched marketing traditions of the Old World in favor of developing their own ways," said the Herr Professor Grundig.

"*Ja,*" said Theodor. "Americans weren't hampered by a predetermined market strategy."

"That must be what's meant by Yankee ingenuity," Frau Strom commented.

"*Natürlich!*" said the Herr Professor. "Roebling talked about maximum utility with minimum labor."

"*Jawohl!*" agreed the Frau Professor Grundig. "And more than that. It's also seeing the potentiality of a larger market, that the enjoyment of basic comforts should not be limited to the upper classes but should be available to all."

"*Richtig!*" Adolf wanted to add his electrical knowledge. "There's the story of Heinrich Goebel, who dabbled with the incandescent lamp before Thomas Edison."[135]

The Frau Professor summarized, "Embellished and implemented in the New Country."

"But I think it will be even more interesting in the coming years," said the Herr Professor Grundig, "to see how these ideas pass back and forth across the Atlantic."

"*Jawohl!*" Theodor's eyes were now sparkling at his companions' interest. "We can look forward to cross currents."

At that moment Stefan reappeared, and having heard the last, chimed in. "Have any of you read Mark Twain's book *A Connecticut Yankee in King Arthur's Court?*[136] The hero attempts to revolutionize Europe's so-called medieval manners but his efforts are all in vain."

The others saw a thoughtful look growing on Michael's face. His critical remark surprised them. "I suppose the methodical, time-consuming way of craftsmanship competes with a market bent on the quick, mechanical method of industrialism."

"*Das ist es eigentlich!*" Theodor said, as the men in the group turned to observe him more closely. "It seems to me that the whole system of economics is being turned upside down."

"Isn't that going to mean that quality will be sacrificed?" asked Herr Strom, thinking of the craftsmanship that went into Daimler Benz cars.

Theodor paused before continuing more quietly. "We'll have to see. Certainly most of us craftsmen won't want to see our training go to waste." To himself he thought—I wonder what effect that's going to have on woodworking.

"*Richtig!*" said Stefan, "after having spent so many years learning it."

Adolf shook his head "I don't think mine is going to go to waste."

"*Ja, du bist ein Glückspilz!* The field of electricity is just getting started," said Stefan.

Suddenly food odors from the stands began commanding their attention, making them realize that their meager breakfast had been depleted. The conversation went in the direction of needs. "*Ich habe Hunger,*" and "*Ja, ich auch,*" were comments making the rounds among them.

Frau Kummer said, "But let's buy our tickets first, and get that over with."

Walter said, "I think before anything we have to exchange money, *nicht wahr?* Unless you already have dollars." When Walter saw how many shook their heads, he said, "It's on to the Money Exchange then." A few had already tried the food booths putting forth their European currency only to discover it did not work here.

"*Stimmt's,*" said Walter. "Native money and postage stamps are of no value here."

As the knowledge sunk in, they made their way to the booth which included the word they recognized—*Geldwechsel.* Walter suggested, "Let's look at the exchange rate for today, so we know what to calculate."

Upon seeing the table, the brothers were shocked. "*Schaut mal!*" said

Adolf. "The rate has plunged even lower." The whole group stood in silence for a moment. Finally Theodor ventured, "I hope our families back home are doing all right."

"That's the wish of us all," murmured the Seligmanns. Everyone suddenly cast their eyes downward. Thinking about their starving relatives back home took away the appetite they had talked about but a moment ago.

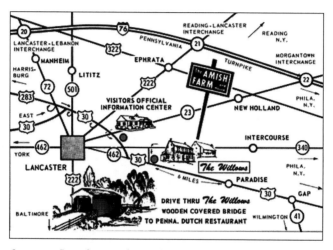

Lancaster, Pennsylvania, where a large number of Pennsylvania Dutch, or Amish, live.

NEW COUNTRY TRAIN TRIP

"Our trip westward will occur within the German quadrangle," Walter announced, once they were settled in the train. "What's that?" asked Hans Grundig, his alert eyes sparkling with curiosity.

"Well, *Hänschen*, that's the part of the United States where the majority of German immigrants have settled. And it's shaped like a rectangle. How many corners in a rectangle?"

Hans' voice bubbled into a chuckle. "*Vier.*"

"*Richtig!* So we're going to have four corners here, too, but since they're not even, we call it a quadrangle, instead of a rectangle."

"How many degrees are the angles of a rectangle?" asked his father.

"Ninety," the boy answered quickly.

"*Richtig!* But here some angles have more, some less," said the Herr Professor.

"Well then, the sides can't be even either," remarked his son.

"*Du hast recht, Kleiner.*" Walter called, "*Pass auf,* Stefan! Do you have the map that Herr Offizier Niederung gave us?" The lanky youth slipped it from his breast pocket and handed it to Walter. "So, gather 'round," said Walter, "and let's take a look." He laid the map flat and asked, "Who has a piece of string?" Herr Seligmann dug into his pocket and from its creases drew a short, grayish piece of fluff.

"*Großartig!* So at each of the four corners there is an important city. We'll start with New York here in the northeast, where we are now, then we move westward to Minneapolis and St. Paul." At the mention of the

Twin Cities, Theodor, Adolf, and Michael perked up. Walter laid the string straight between the Cities and New York. "Then it goes south to St. Louis." He angled the string.

"That's where we're going," said *Hänschen*, "*nicht wahr, Vati?*"

The Herr Professor Grundig nodded to his son, and Walter said, "*Richtig, Hans*. Then we turn back east to Baltimore. And to complete the quadrangle we go back up north to New York."

Hans retraced the route with his index finger, while Frau Kummer exclaimed, "*Das ist ja hoch interessant!*" The others started at the first positive statement they had heard from her.

Hans volunteered, "So most of us will end up living inside the string."

As they talked, exhaustion was overcoming them. They had stowed their baggage all about their space—in the aisles, in overhead carriers, underneath their seats. Some were even leaning on suitcases for lack of room or for reasons of security. Theodor and Adolf had positioned Theodor's precious box between them on their seat and had attached it on either side with a cord to the wrist, so they would be alerted to any attempt to remove the package while they slept. They had taken out the box from the trunk to check on it after their trunk was examined by customs inspectors. Then the contents in the trunk had shifted and they couldn't get the box back in quickly. Finally they decided the short distance didn't merit the trouble of repacking.

Now the excitement of landing had abated and the ordeal at Ellis Island had vaporized, though the odor of the machine oil at the station still lingered. Before them lay a new unknown. However, contemplating the next step could wait. As the train moved forward, its undulating movement lulled them into deep sleep.

Theodor was the first among the group to awaken. He felt totally refreshed. He didn't know how much time he had slept. He would have to wait for Walter to wake up to have him consult his watch. Meanwhile, Theodor looked out the window, so as not to miss any more of the passing fall colors. The seasons come earlier here—he thought.

A short while later Adolf opened his eyes and would merely have turned over except that he caught Theodor awake at the window. He sat up and yawned. "Been awake long?"

"A while."

"What have you been doing?" Adolf asked, although overcome by the desire to go back to sleep.

Theodor shrugged. "Just looking and thinking."

Adolf took one glance out the window and said, "Wake me up if we come to a city or something." He turned away, pulling the box's cord in his direction, so that Theodor was forced to lean to one side. He didn't blame Adolf. His tender stomach still bothered him a bit. Theodor merely loosened the cord on his side of the box, so he could move closer to the window.

The New Country landscape seemed so similar to that of the Old Country that Theodor was suddenly struck with homesickness. He could picture Friedrich, Anna, Maria, and his mother working in the fields—late vegetables here mostly, he surmised, that extended across most of his view, broken now and then by straw-yellow patches, which must be grain fields. There were also tall green plants that he didn't recognize. Suddenly the faces of Annerl and little Heinrich arose amidst the misty memories and the faces of his master teacher, his best friend, and other close members in the town.

Was this new land really going to mean opportunity for him and for Adolf? Some immigrants did not make a successful adjustment in the New Country, like Walter's aunt, for instance, despite its offerings. Others Theodor had heard about made such a financial success of their move that they returned in a short time to the Old Country, lavishing gifts on the relatives they had left behind.

The train slowed as it approached a settlement. As they came closer, splashes of color settled into outlines of stores and houses. They seemed to be all wood frame objects, even the church. The new arrivals had never seen a wooden church before. Old Country churches were massive and solid, made out of stone. Even their little village chapel was not of wood.—But wood means more work for me, thought Theodor gleefully.

Now as the train slowed even more, its convulsive moves jerked its sleepers awake. They saw a church spire and an American flag penetrating the sky above the treetops. A tall, gray, cement cylinder came next into view. Walter said the cylinder was for storing grain and they soon saw that the flag denoted a post office.

The train started up again. Theodor said, "We must be in Pennsylvania by now."

"*Jawohl!*" Walter answered, observing his friend's tense position, as if he were poised to action.

"We'll be stopping soon to let the Seligmanns off," said Walter. In a corner the couple were busy collecting their belongings.

Theodor sighed. "It's such a shame to pass through all this territory and not see the great places."

"*Ach*, Theodor, just let us get this part behind us," said his brother, eyes full of sleep.

But Fräulein Strom, maintaining the trend of teasing Theodor about his longings, said, "I suppose you wanted to see Philadelphia." Her blue eyes held a challenge for him to answer.

"*Jawohl!* That was the site of the first fair where the world began to notice America," Theodor answered evenly, then said, "Even nicer would have been to see Germantown."[137]

"Germantown? Hm-m." Herr Strom's curiosity showed in his face. "Does that mean that it was founded by Germans?"

"*Jawohl!* That was also in that book I read before I left."

"But I thought Germany had no colonies," exclaimed Walter.

As he spoke the Seligmanns had rejoined the group. The Frau replied, "But it wasn't a colony in control of a foreign government, like the French or the English."

"Or the Dutch or the Spanish," Herr Seligmann added. "Our early settlers were trying to escape religious persecution like the Quakers did in England."

"Would that be the Amish?" Walter ventured finally.

"Yes," said Herr Seligmann. "In the sixteen hundreds[138] we got permission from William Penn to settle in Pennsylvania."

His wife added, "We just wanted to worship as we saw fit, in a way meaningful to us."

"Maybe you heard of Franz Daniel Pastorius."[139] Herr Seligmann looked around the group, but got no recognition. "Well, anyway, he organized the Atlantic trip and founded Germantown."

Walter said, "How do you get along with the Pennsylvania Dutch?"[140] The Seligmanns both laughed. "You see, we are the Dutch, the Pennsylvania Dutch. That's another name for us." Frau Seligmann had an amused look on her face.

"Oh," said Walter, "so the Pennsylvania Dutch are really German?"

"*Richtig!*" asserted Frau Seligmann.

Her husband said, "The Dutch have the mouth of the Rhine River, whereas we're from a little farther south on the Rhine in Germany."

Through the train window they could see the horse and buggy that had come for them. Frau Kummer nudged the couple, nodding in the direction of the waiting buggy.

"*Ja, ja,* Frau Kummer." The couple looked around at the whole group. "*Sehr schön, Sie alle kennengelernt zu haben,*" they said, shaking hands all around. "*Auf Wiedersehen!*"

"*Hoffentlich!*" the travelers responded. Tears began showing. The first couple to leave the train made them realize this was it. There was little hope of ever meeting again. "Nice to have known you too," they responded. When Frau Seligmann reached Herr Kraenke, she bent down to embrace him. "*Alles Gute im Neuen Land!*"

With her promise for optimism, he straightened up. "*Es wird schon gehen.*"

The couple seated themselves in the buggy. The driver in black top hat and suit was accompanied by a woman in black hood and long skirt, the somber colors relieved only by white shirts, which appeared clean and starched despite the dusty, dirt road on which they traveled. As the rest turned back, they murmured what a nice pair they had made. It was a moment before Fräulein Strom commented, "*Na schön,* I still would prefer a Daimler Benz to a buggy."

"*Gewiß!*" some said, although most could not envision any car at all in the near future.

Meanwhile, Theodor surveyed the landscape. "I can see why this land would appeal to the Pennsylvania Dutch. It's very similar to the landscape in their original territory around the middle Rhine." It seemed odd to speak with firsthand authority about a geographical fact. Theodor was thinking—we've actually seen the Rhenish countryside.

The earlier discussion left Hans' inquisitive mind pondering. "I don't understand how the Dutch can be German."

Herr Professor Grundig paused to formulate an answer his son could understand. "It's like this. Both are on the Rhine River. Holland, which was originally a part of the Holy Roman Empire, had broken away. You know that the Rhine River mouths into the North Sea in Holland. So the *Niederländer,* or Lowlanders, are from the lowland coast. But the *Rheinländer* are from farther south on the Rhine in what is today Germany."

"Explain to us then why the Americans call them Dutch?" asked Walter.

The Herr Professor Grundig spoke. "Nobody really knows. But there are two main theories. The first is that the immigrants spoke lowland German and the lowland word for German is pronounced 'Dutch'. The second is that in written form, they used the standard word for German, which is Deutsch. When English speakers saw the written term, however, they probably didn't know what to do with the pronunciation of 'eu' in German, so they disregarded the 'e' and pronounced only the 'u.' The word 'Dutch' is probably a distortion of our word '*Deutsch.*'"

His wife added, "And that word originally meant the 'people.'"

"But they didn't know that 'eu' becomes the sound 'oy' in English." [141]

"Oh, like in the English word 'boy,'" Hans said brightly. "That's what I am, a boy."

The adults looked at the child. Someone said, "Spelled b-e-u!" They all laughed heartily, having often seen his parents studying books in English with him.

"*Das ist schön, Hänschen!*" Walter praised. "You just keep right on learning English."

MIDWEST MEDLEY

𝒜fter the group had dropped off in Pittsburgh the families with men who hoped to work in the steel mills, the passengers crossed the remainder of the Alleghenies, then left off Herr Kraenke and others in Ohio. Next they left off the Stroms and others in Detroit. When the train started moving again, those remaining teased, "Theodor, don't you want to join them to see Ford's factory?"

"Actually, I would," he said, then more emphatically, "*Natürlich!* I would like to see the New Country assembly lines." The phenomenon was not as developed in the Old Country.

After a bit, Walter said, "It won't be long now before it's time to leave for the rest of us."

"I hope so. The scenery has been all the same." Frau Kummer's hands were so restless, the others wanted to supply her with crochet or knitting needles.

Nevertheless, the brothers agreed. "Fields," said Adolf, "nothing but fields. The first few days were okay, but day after day there's been nothing but fields."

"*Jawohl!*" Theodor had chosen to stand awhile, and now he rocked back and forth on his feet. "Fields for miles and miles. Quite different from the Old Country, at least for us on the trip north."

Stefan agreed. "Every time you looked out the window, in 'Deutschland' the view was different." Everyone giggled at his comparison.

Walter defended. "It's America's bread basket! Lots of grain fields."

"But where are all the farmers?" the rest insisted.

"What do you mean?" asked Walter. "They're on their farms."

"But there is no evidence of human habitation," said the Herr Professor Grundig.

"*Jawohl!*" Theodor pointed to some buildings in the distance. "You don't see any people." He scanned the horizon. "That little clump of color ahead is not big enough to be a farm village."

"Maybe they're just smaller villages than what we're used to," said Michael.

Walter corrected, "No, no, it's a single farm all right."

As they got nearer, Adolf said, "The layout still puzzles me. It's only a single house and a barn, some sheds maybe in the middle of some fields."

"*Richtig!* That doesn't make sense to me either," said Stefan.

Walter thought a minute. "Maybe it doesn't, but the pattern is most likely due to the homesteading tradition, whereby a farmer was granted a tract of land to work. If he succeeded with his plot, he would be given that land. That's how they 'peopled' America."

Theodor's eyes began twitching as his earnestness grew. "But the farms are so far from any town. How do they shop?"

Soon the others were challenging with questions.

"How do they get their mail?" asked Stefan.

Walter said, "They have what's called Rural Free Delivery."[142]

Theodor looked aghast. "They deliver to every isolated farm? That seems wasteful."

"*Ach,* you Swabians and your constant thoughts on frugality," exclaimed Stefan.

Walter corrected, "I don't think they drive in to each house; rather several farms have a common location."

"So they still go some distance to get their mail. In our little village the postboxes are all at the entrance of the farm community a few steps away for all of us," said Adolf. "The chapel is also there, so Sunday service is not a problem."

"*Ja,* I was wondering how the farmers get to church," said the Frau Professor.

"And how do they get a doctor, or a pastor?" asked Frau Kummer.

"Just a house, a barn, and other outbuildings? Isn't that a bit impractical?" asked Theodor.

Adolf turned to Theodor. "*Genau!* Besides being more windy. But, *lieber Bruder,* that's what our Onkels wrote us, remember? They said the farm is about fifteen kilometers from town."

Walter calculated roughly. "That's about ten miles. *Ja,* you may have to arrange your schedule differently."

Indeed, it was beginning to register on the newcomers what was meant by everything being a greater distance in the New Country, which would also account for a less exciting topography from their viewpoint.

"It seems like a long way when one runs out of flour or sugar," finished the Frau Professor. The brothers thought to themselves—such staples could be bought right in Daisendorf. Sure, fifteen kilometers was not an impossible walk, but for every little errand?

Slowly the landscape was becoming more populated, and soon thereafter they saw converging railroad tracks. "We're arriving in Chicago," Theodor predicted.

"*Jawohl!* I didn't know it was going to be so large. It's looking as busy as New York," Frau Kummer said. "All those platforms, railroad tracks, and people running around."

The conductor, who they learned shortly had come as a German immigrant twenty years ago just like the brothers' uncles, approached. "*Das ist Chicago. Hier müssen Sie umsteigen.*"

The announcement struck the transferees with ambiguous feelings, for Chicago meant saying good-bye to more of them. They were scattering in all directions, some staying in Chicago, some going north to Wisconsin cities with German-sounding names, like Rhinelander, some heading southward, one family even as far as New Braunfels, Texas. A few, like the Grundigs and Walter, were bound for St. Louis. Others were going to points westward as far as the journey's end to San Francisco or to the forests of Washington state.

It was obvious the *Hannover* travelers lamented their farewell, for in their short time together they had developed a kinship. On the other hand, they knew the departure brought closer their union with their waiting relatives, and their start of a new life.

"*Auf Wiedersehen! Auf Wiedersehen!*" could be heard in various German dialects. They refused to say good-bye, only that they might see each other again. Suddenly Hans Grundig had Theodor's legs locked in a hug. Theodor bent down to lift him up so they could see eye to eye. Theodor's eyes misted as he put Hans down.

Finally, the brothers turned to Walter.

"Well," said the brothers, "this is it." After their last slow-paced weeks, the time seemed suddenly to race. The conductor had already returned from accompanying departing passengers to their next trains and was looking to help others. It was strange how after all this time the good-byes sped by them. Walter was hastily writing his address on a scrap of paper. The Grundigs didn't have a permanent place, but the university would know where to find them. The brothers were saying, "Eden Valley, that's all you have to know. No address needed, no phone."

Then everybody was embracing everybody else. When Theodor got to Walter, he said, "You've been such a good travel companion." He would like to have said much more, what good company he had been, how his knowledge had inspired him with ideas he intended to carry out, and so on. But Adolf was urging him onward, indicating the conductor patiently standing at the exit. Nearly everybody was gone. Even Stefan and Michael were already waiting outside the train.

The conductor accompanied them into the station, then pointed the way to connecting trains. He indicated the clock high above in the station. They thought—*Gott sei Dank!* We can keep track of the time.

They learned they had two hours until their next train.

Once they had a chance to get their bearings inside the station, they realized that the hectic transfer was already behind them. The wistful farewells gave way to a wonderland of never-seen-before objects: toys, gadgets, snacks. At a produce stand were fruits and vegetables, some they had never seen in the Old Country. Theodor's eyes finally landed on an object he did know. "Look at the sign, Adolf! The word for *Apfel* is 'apple,' almost like *appel* in Low German."

"What are you talking about?" asked Michael and Stefan.

"Oh, we've just been noticing that the English word is often closer to Low German along the coast in the north than it is to our Upper German in the south." said Adolf.

"*Ja*, now that you mention it, I've noticed that too," said Michael.

"*Schaut mal!* What are those funny, crooked, yellow things? Are they for eating?"

Noticing the boys' interest, the peddler spoke the word "banana" several times. Adolf nodded in recognition, "*Richtig, Banane!*"

The peddler put a banana to his mouth and made chewing motions. Do you eat the peeling too? Theodor motioned. The peddler shook his head, showing how to peel the banana. He ate the inside, then threw the peel in the trash can.

"Do you want to try them?" Besides Theodor, only Stefan wanted one.

Theodor took out the American coins they had gotten in New York. "*Nur twee*," said Theodor, trying out his Low German, but at the same time holding up thumb and forefinger.

"Yes, just one?" asked the peddler.

"*Nein, twee, twee*," said Theodor, wondering what had gone wrong this time.

"Oh, two?" But instead of holding up thumb and forefinger, the peddler held up index and middle finger as he plucked two from a bunch. Even the sign language must be different. But in the end Theodor was pleased with his successful purchase.

Stefan summarized, "Two is certainly closer to *twee* in Low German than *twee* to *zwei* in High German."

At first the peel didn't budge for them, but soon the two snackers caught on to piercing the skin first to get the peel started. "Not bad, I guess," said one. "A little dry," said the other. They bit into the peeling just to test it. No, it definitely was not edible.

As they continued walking, they came to a vendor selling a white substance sitting in a hard shell. Ice cream, the sign read. What could that be? "*Sicher!*" Theodor exclaimed. "*Eis!*"

"Yes," the vendor said, "ice CREAM."

But it sure didn't look like the ice they knew. The man wasn't sure they had the idea, so he gestured how you held the container, which they couldn't tell if it was paper or dough and enjoyed the scoop of ice cream on top by sliding your tongue around it. He allowed them to sample some.

"It's cold! Colder than whipped cream!" Theodor exclaimed. "*Aber es schmeckt gut!*" Then he said in English, "Two," and this time he didn't even use his fingers. Stefan and Michael followed suit, delighted that their "two" was understood.

By the time they got down to the cone, they were some distance from the stand. "What do we do with the shell?"

Theodor turned the cone to all sides. "Beats me. Do you suppose it's to eat?"

Adolf shrugged and threw it away. They all followed suit.

After they finished seeing everything, they still had time before departure.

"So, now you're headed for Wisconsin," said Theodor to Stefan.

"*Jawohl!*" said Stefan "The state from which several regiments for the Civil War[143] were predominantly German immigrants, including my great uncle."

"In the American Civil War?" asked Theodor. "How did he wind up there?"

"He was a Forty-Eighter."

"*Ach, ich verstehe,*" said Michael. "And when the Revolution in Frankfurt failed in 1848, he was one that had to flee for his life?"

"Yes, along with thousands of others, he fled to America.[144] You've probably never heard of Carl Schurz, but I've heard about him often in my uncle's letters. He was the most famous Forty-Eighter,[145] and he started out in Wisconsin. And his wife, Margaret was also prominent. She founded America's first Kindergarten."[146] They went on discussing the state's bonds with their country, until it was time for Stefan's departure.

Soon the Soo Line train was negotiating the morainal hills of Wisconsin. As the train moved on, the three young men became sleepy. When the two brothers woke up, they were crossing a river with the

The village of Eden Valley, Minnesota, in the twenties.

most spectacular rock formations. Theodor pointed out the river to a passing conductor, who said, "That's the Mississippi." For a river of major importance, as they had learned, it didn't look impressive, but the rocks intrigued them.

They must be getting close to their destination. Their uncles had mentioned the river in their letters. The conductor held up one finger indicating it was still an hour to their destination. They had to remember distances were greater here. Anyway, it was not too early to change into their good clothes. As soon as they had boarded, they had all drawn from their baggage their suits to hang out. Their clothes were wrinkled, but at least not smudged. Now they brushed them, trying to get out the last wrinkles.

They found a place to change. As Theodor returned to his seat, he thought—Here I am in the New World, wearing the suit of a man who lost his life in the Old World. . . .

By the time the conductor called, "The Twin Cities: Minneapolis, St. Paul!" they had even repacked their suitcases. Excitement welled up in them. They were close to the end!

Arriving in the station, the brothers scanned the spectators, but there wasn't anyone who looked like the pictures their relatives had sent. Michael found his relatives right away. His party seemed in a hurry to depart. Michael was going south, but the brothers were going north. "Look me up in New Ulm," he called back upon leaving them.

Suddenly the brothers noticed a sign, which said: R-I-T-S-C-H-E. "That's got to be us. No one else would have such a spelling."

"*Ich weiß nicht!* The person holding it looks rather young to be our aunt."

"*Richtig!*" The woman with the sign came up to them and asked, "*Wie war die Reise, Jungen?*"

The boys perked up. They understood her sentence! How was the trip, boys? "I am Elizabeth. I live here in Minneapolis." After they had shaken hands, she went on in German to explain. "I'm going to accompany you on the train to Eden Valley, since I'm going to visit my parents who also live there. They are friends of your uncles. Your family will surely be at the train station in Eden Valley to greet you."

Elizabeth looked at the overladen boys. She wasn't about to offer a hand with the trunk, but she thought she could lighten Theodor's load. She asked, "Can I carry the package for you?"

"No, no," Theodor said, clutching his box more tightly. "I can manage."

"We have to go this way to catch our train to Eden Valley." What? they thought—another train? Not a car, a streetcar, or even a horse and buggy?

The boys had thought somehow that Eden Valley[147] was right there, near the Cities. Now they realized they had still another leg to the trip. "*Wie lang ist die Reise?*" they couldn't help asking.

"Oh, the trip is not long at all. Only an hour or so."

After five weeks underway, they realized, an hour was not much additional time. But Theodor had been counting. The train trip would be the seventh transfer of luggage. However, they had arrived safely, and, best of all, they no longer had to be so watchful. They were finally in the hands of someone who knew where she was going.

The brothers made their way to their train and were in the act of ascending the steps, when a policeman approached and asked to see their papers. Luggage peeking out from their figures in all directions, the boys asked Elizabeth, "*Was ist los?*" Safe? Suddenly their insecurity surfaced again.

The policeman was already viewing their documents, passports, and tickets, as well as Elizabeth's identification. The thought ran through Elizabeth's mind, What are we going to do? We don't have a match in surnames. But she managed to say to the boys, "*Nichts.* He just wants to make sure that I'm not kidnapping you. The newspaper says we're having difficulties over that with immigrants lately."

The brothers laughed, at which the policeman looked up from his perusal. Their faces straightened immediately. It wouldn't do to have the policeman thinking they were taking the situation lightly. Suddenly Elizabeth reached energetically into her satchel and triumphantly withdrew the placard. When the policeman saw it, he smiled. It matched the boys' names on their documents.

As they got on the train she said to them in German, "Lucky I kept that placard with your name on it. I just about threw it out. It proved we belonged together. Nobody would ever make up a name like yours."

The boys had to agree. At last, settled in the train, the discomforts of the trip suddenly vanished. Relief took hold of the boys and with it the relaxation of bones, muscles, nerves. It was early afternoon. The sun shone brightly, showing off the landscape in its best light. Except for some trivial conversation now and then, the boys were content to watch the rich farmland flow by their window. In the spring the black loamy soil would set off lush, green crops. What would they be doing by spring?

EPISODE TWENTY-FOUR

HERZLICH WILLKOMMEN IN EDEN VALLEY.

As Elizabeth had promised, in a little over an hour they stopped at a small railroad station. A sign in print just large enough for passengers to read as the train passed by said Eden Valley. The platform was vacant except for three figures. Even in the distance the boys recognized them as their relatives from the photos they had sent.

"*Herzlich Willkommen in* Eden Valley," said Onkel Martin, as they descended.

"Here they are, safe and sound," their young guide announced.

"*Jawohl, heil und sicher! Tante Maria! Onkel Martin! Onkel Anton!*" the boys said, approaching them with open arms.

Maria's greeting was much the same as Elizabeth's in Minneapolis, only she did not say 'boys,' but rather 'nephews.' "*Wie war die Reise, Neffen?*"

"*Lang,*" they answered simply, yet one could feel the entire five weeks in the word's tone.

Elizabeth shared some bits of news about Minneapolis. Maria brought out a gift for Elizabeth, some doilies she had crocheted herself. They talked a little more.

"Well," said their guide. "I shall be off to my parents' then."

"*Grüß die Eltern von uns. Und vielen Dank.*"

"Yes, my parents will appreciate your greeting. *Auf Wiedersehen!*" She turned in the direction of her parents' house.

Martin took his nephews' baggage from them.

Martin Moehrle and his wife Maria Brulla

Not seeing any conveyance, Adolf asked, "Will we be walking to the farm?"

"Walking, no. You're not in Europe anymore. Come along. I'll show you."

Around the corner of the station, horses and a wagon awaited them. Anton said, *"Bis später!"*

The boys looked after him with a puzzled expression. "He's not coming with us?"

"Nein, he lives here in the village. He'll pick up his daughters, then come to the farm."

Theodor asked, "How is Onkel Anton faring since his wife passed away?"

"Gut," answered Tante Maria. "And the three girls are a great help."

As they all got in the wagon, Onkel Martin said, "It's a half-hour ride to the farm."

The boys thought, mistaken once again, *Noch eine Strecke.* Number eight. It seemed always one more stretch, one more leg. Well, that's right, according to the landscapes they had seen on their way west, the farm would be some distance from the village. It would be one of those lone farms they had observed in the middle of farm fields. The dirt road was rocky and full of pitholes, so that the passengers bumped back and forth on their wooden slat seats. Sometimes the boys even lost their balance.

"*Ja, Achtung!*" Tante Maria warned.

Around a number of bends in the road the farm finally came into view. They turned off the main road into their farm. Adolf said, "And there's the country mailbox."

"*Jawohl!*" Onkel Martin said. "R.F.D."

"But didn't they spell your name wrong?" Theodor asked. "The box said Moehrle."

"*Jawohl!* It's changed from *Möhrle*. English has no *Umlaut*."[148] They went through the pronunciation of the surname in America before reaching the farm.

The layout of the several structures seemed haphazard to the boys, unlike in the Old Country, where the outbuildings were really out. Around a clearing stood house, barn, and other sheds, which they later learned were chicken coop, pigsty, and granary, all arranged in circular fashion.

Finally the wagon came to a stop in front of a white frame two-story house. "*Wir sind zum Haus und Hof angekommen,*" announced Tante Maria.

So this was going to be hearth and home. The brothers didn't know what to expect from their "kith and kin." But the minute they stepped inside, something resonated within them, as if the homestead took over where the last had left off. The kitchen smelled of sugar and spice, and did they detect the odor of real coffee? Their last walk through Meersburg, with its delicious odors, flashed through their minds, and the memory of the real coffee that their sister Emilie had arranged.

The cast iron stove gave off a cozy warmth to the cool fall day. Through the doorway of the room beyond they could see some greenery and a wooden chair arm, which looked like it could belong to a rocking chair. But they focused on the large plank kitchen table, already set for eleven places as if it were especially meant for such grand occasions.

Son Joe came in from the barn, where he had been milking cows. Daughters Louise and Christine came down from upstairs, where they had been finishing up the room the boys would occupy. Their three cousins seemed to be close in age, all in their middle teens, a year or two younger than Theodor. The girls curtsied their introductions and Joe shook hands.

"By the time you get the boys settled, Martin, we'll have the table ready," Maria said in German. "And Anton and the girls will be here."

From an ice chest she took a deep bowl of cream to whip into *Schlagsahne*. Theodor's mouth was already watering at the idea of whipped cream.—*Das wird gut schmecken,* he thought to himself. Adolf, too, seemed impressed.

Martin led them upstairs to their room. It seemed large to them for only two people. "Are you sure we aren't pushing someone out?"

Martin answered, "Not at all. Christine and Louise like sharing a room. And Joe has cut out his own space." The boys wondered to themselves,—each girl had her own room? They thought of their Old Country home with its minimal number of bedrooms.

When the travelers returned from upstairs, the whipped cream was now absent, probably being kept in a cool place until serving time. The two had retrieved from their suitcases the gifts their mother had sent. The "4711" cologne brought notes of approval.

But the sight of the bottles of *Weißherbst* seemed to circulate a secret message among their newfound relatives. The latest edition of Dr. Oetker cookbooks brought oohs and aahs from their aunt, and everybody loved the various carved wooden pieces from the *Schwarzwald*.

Just then they saw another horse and buggy in the distance. Anton and the girls were arriving. Soon they entered the house and there was a grand shaking of hands all around. The nephews met Anton's daughters, Maria, Alice, and Frieda. A ceremony began about who was to sit where. In the end it was decided, except for Tante Maria, who had the torte and the cake plates ready at the foot of the table, that the young people would sit on the sides intermittently between new relatives, so they would all have a better chance to get acquainted.

"*Schaut, meine Nichten!* Your cousins have brought us a Dr. Oetker cookbook."

The nieces marveled at the pictures but hesitated at the recipes. Finally one said, "We'll have to convert the measurements."

The boys looked puzzled. "*Wie so denn?*"

"We don't use weights for cooking here in America, but rather amounts." The boys looked about the kitchen. Sure enough there was no scale. *Schade!* Mother had not foreseen a different method of measurement.

Tante Maria said, "*Keine Sorge! Ich helfe Euch. Das wird Spaß machen!*"

When the girls heard that they would have fun doing the conversions with Tante Maria, they cheered up. The six women would make a day of it in the kitchen, say at Christmas time.

Tante Maria set on the kitchen table an *Obsttorte*, that she had made. The boys thought—why it's just like home, for our last *Kaffeepause* in Daisendorf. The difference was that although it would be serving about the same number of people, the torte was huge in comparison with theirs, but no more decorated.

A flat, round layer of sponge-like cake with a thin, slightly-raised edge held a topping of assorted canned or cooked fruit. Tante Maria had arranged the fruit in a gigantic flower pattern, with pale red cherries in the middle for the flower center and sliced pears, plums, and peaches in circular fashion, white, purple, and orange, fanning out from the middle like petals. Around the edges she had used pale green gooseberries, placed to resemble leaves. A gelatinous substance poured over the top held the fruit in place. It all looked so homey on its pedestal platter.

The boys couldn't help commenting, "*Jawohl!*"

Tante Maria continued in German, "The gooseberries, pears, and plums are our own home-grown." Her figure was bursting with pride.

"It's just like Mother makes, right, Theodor?" Adolf asked.

"*Ja,* the same fruit and everything." Theodor was thinking—it's a continuation from home. Only here, real coffee was probably served everyday.

"That's because I brought the fruit stock from Austria." They were reminded of Maria's native country.

"Later the girls can take you around the farm to show you the orchard, the berry bushes, and so on," added Onkel Martin.

While Tante Maria slipped pieces of torte on cake plates, Louise and Christine poured coffee from two pots, one girl on either side. The boys noticed that the pots matched the plate pattern. In the Old Country they had a conglomeration of designs in their dishware, from here and there, some inherited, some bought, and others for which they didn't even know the origin. So much had gone by the wayside during the Great War.

The large bowl of whipped cream had been retrieved from somewhere cool and now was passed. When the bowl got to Adolf and Theodor, Tante Maria jumped up from her seat, seized the bowl from their hands and put extra dollops on their torte. "We have to fatten you up. You're too skinny after the boat trip."

When the last person was served, they all gave a toast to the brothers: "*Viel Glück im Neuen Land!*" After wishing them lots of luck in the New Country, at last they could indulge their watering palates.

"*Schmeckt das?*" asked Tante Maria.

"Yes, it tastes really good," the boys enthused. The first sip from their cups inspired a clandestine signal between the two brothers across the table to indicate "*Echter Kaffee.*" The family must indeed be in a favorable position. In the Old Country only the well-off enjoyed real coffee daily, the brothers were thinking. As if reading their thoughts, one of Anton's daughters said, "Here we can have coffee every day."

Onkel Anton asked, "What about beer?"

"Beer?" uttered Theodor, eager to let them know the status of the German contribution to beverages. "Prewar it was thirteen pennies a glass, postwar it went to seventeen Marks."

Adolf filled them in on the status of potatoes.

Onkel Anton laughed. "That figures. Potatoes went up three times, whereas beer went up only one-third."

"But that's not all. In the five years since the end of the war, prices have kept on rising. By last year beer was sixty Marks, then last summer it shot up to 3000 Marks, and it's still climbing."[149]

There was a long silence. At last Onkel Anton spoke up to address the real issue. "Well, at least you have it."

"What do you mean?" The brothers looked at them perplexed.

"Haven't you heard about prohibition?[150] We have no legal access to beer," said Onkel Martin.

"Nor wine nor whisky," Onkel Anton added.

The brothers looked aghast. "You can't buy beer?" Adolf said, which Theodor echoed.

The two looked at their new cousins incredulously. "So you've never even tasted beer?" Theodor asked, whereupon the young girls started giggling.

But Onkel Anton broke in. "I merely said we have no legal access to beer."

The nephews leaned back as the thought sunk in. "So there is illegal beer?"

"We have a few farmers, yes, who do some moonshining."

"Moonshining?" the boys echoed.

"*Ja*, it's usually made at night by the light of the moon," said Onkel Anton.

"So how long is this condition going to be around?" asked Adolf.

"We don't know, but it's been in practice for a good three years already, *richtig*, Maria?" said Onkel Martin.

Onkel Anton addressed the immigrants. "Now if you had known that, you wouldn't have come, *richtig, Neffen?*" He laughed.

"Well, some people say the ban is a good thing," Tante Maria insisted. She looked at Anton's three daughters. "If your *Mutter* were here she'd say liquor is too great a temptation. People just can't handle it."

"Hooch, Maria, why don't you just say hooch?" her brother-in-law demanded. "*Ja*, and some people also say the new women's styles are a disgrace, but I rather like them." He sat smugly back in his chair.

"*Ach*, Anton, even the Pope is urging a campaign against the new revealing styles," Maria scolded. "Imagine, showing all their legs."

Anton's three daughters giggled and looked at Louise and Christine to see their reaction.

"But beer, a glass of beer is refreshing after a hard day's work," Theodor insisted.

That night the brothers fell asleep exhausted. It was the first time in almost five weeks that they were able to stretch out to their full length. Although Theodor was slight of build, and therefore didn't have to double up as much as others in cramped spots, he doubted at the moment that he would ever travel that much again. Right now he felt that getting from their hometown in the Old Country to their destination in the New Country was a trip that was going to last him a lifetime.

His last thought before he fell asleep, however, was that, all in all, maybe life in the New Country won't be so different from that in the Old Country. And his mouth watered as he remembered the fruit torte with whipped cream and the real coffee.—Maybe I'm going to like the New Country more than I had thought. But no beer?

Preface

a. Günther Grass:

   http://csmweb2.emcweb.com/durable/1999/
   http://www.csmonitor.com/durable/1999/10/01/fp8s2-csm.shtml
   http://www.nobel.se/literature/laureates/1972/press.html (Heinrich Böll)

b. *Elysée Vertrag: www.goethe.de/fr/nan/deelysee.htm* (The Pact between the Federal Republic of Germany and France prescribes the thoroughly new relationship between the countries in order to end the centuries-long enmity and rivalry. Its programs are primarily aimed at youth. A German-French common fund finances the meeting and exchange of high school and university age students and laborers. [English summary from the German by the author.]) The two countries may well be the Wayshowers toward peaceful interaction for the Twenty-First Century. See also "Neue Perspektiven: Deutsch-Französische Erklärung," *Deutschland*, D Nr. 2/2003, April/Mai.

c. *Nowhere in Africa: www.suntimes.com/output/ebert1/wkp-news-nowhere21f.html*

d. East German Uprising: *www.germantv.de*

e. Deutsche Welle: www.germantv.dw-world.de

f. *http://www.capanamur.org/afghanistan/*

g. Max Kade Institute in Wisconsin: *www.wisc.edu/mki*
   University of Wisconsin-Madison, 901 University Bay Drive, Madison, WI 53705

h. Ursula Hegi's fame began with *Stones from the River*, 1994, which takes place in Germany. *The Vision of Emma Blau* continues the story on American soil as a branch of the family immigrates. *Tearing the Silence*, 1997, is more a documentary, interviewing German Americans as to how they coped with the dark side of their genetic history.

i. Hyperinflation: *www.mwsc.eduorgs/germanclub/inflation2.html.*

Part One: The Old Country

1. The quotation from Johann Wolfgang von Goethe (1749-1832) shows Germany's typical admiration for America and its Revolution in 1776. His contemporary, Friedrich Schiller, also was impressed by America's fight for freedom, going so far as to denounce the sale of Hessian soldiers to the British.

2. Alliterative couplets are common to Germanic languages, the language family to which both German and English belong, along with Danish, Norwegian, Swedish, Flemish, Dutch, Icelandic, and a few other languages. Such *"Stabreim,"* in literal translation, "beginning rhyme," or English "alliteration," occurs throughout the text. Examples in English: tendency to name one's children with the same initial letter: Jack and Jill; and in sayings: hearth and home.

3. Italicized words are in High, or Standard, German, for the beginning German student's benefit, even though the family would have spoken an Upper German dialect. German phrases are rendered in English through rephrasing or replying in close proximity to the German wording, unless the spelling makes the meaning obvious: <*Das ist logisch.*> "That's logical."

4. In 2004 Anna Ritsche Schramm, the author's cousin, was still living in the Meersburg area.

5. This Heinrich (Ritsche), Anna's brother, became a World War II casualty.

6. Maclean, Annie M., *Modern Immigration*, Lippincott, Philadelphia, 1925. The following citation reveals Argentina's desire to encourage foreign settlement. "Número especial en el centenario," *La Nación*, Buenos Aires, Buenos Aires, 1916, p. 366. Art. 25 in the Constitution of 1853 becomes Article 17 in the Constitution of 1949. It states: "The Federal Government shall encourage European immigration; and may not restrict, limit or burden with any tax whatsoever, the entrance into Argentine territory of

foreigners who arrive for the purpose of tilling the soil, improving industries, and introducing and teaching the arts and sciences." (Taken from Ritsche, Marita, *Germans in Argentina*, unpublished, submitted in requirement of Foreign Studies 161-162, University of Minnesota, 1956, p. 4.) The summer of 1955 spent in Argentina was part of the Minnesota SPAN (Student Project for Amity among Nations), one of the earliest such international study programs for university students.

7. *Porteños,* Spanish word meaning occupants of a port city, in this case from Buenos Aires.

8. Two main village formations exist. The "cluster village" (*Haufendorf:* "heap village"), mentioned here, in its purest form has the farm houses built around a hub with the fields fanning out radially from the houses. In the other main type, the "line village," (*Straßendorf:* "street village") the houses are built along a road with the back end of the lot usually bordered by a brook. The first will have proximity to neighbors, but may not have equal access to water and market as in the second. The disadvantage of the second is its lack of proximity to neighbors and local shops.

9. The decimal and the period are reversed in writing numbers.

10. Selig, Robert, *German Life,* "Germans in Russia," Dc/Jy, 00/01, p. 42-44. Non-adjacent fields result as a form of inheritance, called "partible inheritance," or the rule that each child inherits a part of the property, contrary to most of the country where the oldest child inherits the entire property. The former practice occurs mostly in southwest and central Germany. Over time such a law results in fragmentation of farm property. In the eighteenth century such disagreeable inheritance laws, as well as obligatory military conscription, a practice made popular by Napoleon, led many Germans to emigrate, especially to Russia, where military service was not mandated. When Russia also passed such a law, the "Germans from Russia" including the "Volga Germans," as those who lived along the Volga River were called, migrated farther to

the New World. Selig relates also that "impartible inheritance," or the practice of having one heir inherit parental property occurred in Bavaria south of the Danube and in northern Germany.

There is reason to believe that the partible inheritance law goes back to the time of *Charlemagne* (Charles the Great, or *Karl des Großen*) in the ninth century. His empire was ultimately divided among three grandsons. The three part division of land is often considered the forerunner of the eventual foundations for modern central Europe. The territory along the western border of the empire became France with the eastern territory going to the future Germany, The third heir received the middle territory, originally an equitable size, but over time reduced to the area now known as Alsace-Lorraine *(Elsaß*-Lothringen)*. The latter area has passed back and forth several times between the two afore-mentioned modern countries. *ß is the sound 's.' It represents a double 'ss' under certain pronunciation conditions. According to the new *Rechtschreibung*—spelling rules—, it is written as 'ss,' just as the *Umlauts* (ä—ö—ü) are to be written without the diairesis and with an added 'e' (ae—oe—ue). It remains to be seen whether the new rules persevere.

11. The *Jägermeister,* or the "Hunting Master," is in charge of the vegetation and animals within certain areas in the forests. He decides when and for whom the forest is open for hunting.

12. For more information on Atlantic crossing conditions around the turn of the last century, see Reeves, Pamela, *Ellis Island,* Barnes & Noble, N.Y.,1998.

13. Kurt F. Reinhardt, *Germany: Two Thousand Years,* v. II, "The Second Empire and the Weimar Republic," Frederick Ungar, N.Y., 1971, p. 658-661. "The devaluation of the German currency, which had begun during the war, was accelerated in the postwar years by lowering German productive capacity caused by territorial and property losses, the dwindling of foreign trade, the lack of international credits, and the payment of reparations. When the

fall of the mark reached alarming proportions Germany demanded a moratorium on reparations (December1921)." The following month a conference was called "to straighten out the reparations tangle and stabilize the German financial situation." Unfortunately at that time the French cabinet was defeated, "and the violently anti-German Raymond Poincaré became prime minister of France."

[Author's note: despite the age of Reinhardt's book, its validity and pursuit of objectivity are still relevant. In fact, in some ways it is even prophetic: KFR 630. "The Hague conferences owed their greatest and lasting achievement, the creation of the Permanent World Court of Arbitration, to the initiative and the political realism of George W. Holls, the secretary of the United States delegation. The weakness of the Hague Tribunal rested in the absence of any legal supranational power which could compel nations to submit their disagreements to arbitration as well as in the fact that the court itself was without any legal means to enforce its decisions. The chief gain, then, was almost entirely on the moral side: the creation of the Hague Tribunal aided in rallying large sections of world opinion in support of the idea of international justice, solidarity, and co-operation." Since Reinhardt will be quoted most often, the reference to him hereafter will be KFR and page number.]

14. **"The German Hyperinflation of 1923:**
A Seventy-Fifth Anniversary Retrospective."
(Website: www.mwsc.edu/~engdept/german/inflation.html)

A. January 1919-June 1922

The worth was in "Jan. 1919 . . . 8.9 Marks to the dollar; Jan. 1922 . . . 191.8 to the dollar . . . In April 1921 the Allies presented Germany with a reparations bill of 132 billion gold marks (31.4 billion dollars) to be paid over a number of years in the form of both money and goods. After another government crisis and the occupation by French troops in the city of Duisburg . . . the [Weimar]

Reich government agreed to yield to the Allied dictum. That decision began a no-win tug-of-war that lasted the next two-and-one-half years and brought German society to the brink of disintegration. There was almost universal agreement among German labor, business, and government leaders that Germany's gross national product was simply not large enough to bear additional obligations of 132 billion German marks.* Moreover, the reparations bill itself accelerated the inflation rapidly out of control. In June 1922 the dollar stood at 350 marks, in October it had risen to 4,500 per dollar." (1998 = 75th anniversary)

*31.4 billion in dollars even with inflation is a huge increase; compare with French indemnity, 1871, # 107, p. 230.

B. January 1923-November 1923

"The German Hyperinflation of 1923: A Seventy-Fifth Anniversary Retrospective . . . passive resistance opened floodgates of uncontrolled inflation. Between early January and November 15, 1923, when inflation was finally brought under control, the German mark in relation to the U.S. dollar fell from an already unprecedented 18,000 to the dollar to an astronomical 4.2 trillion. The social and economic consequences of state-sponsored inflation were enormous and disastrous. Tax collections (and government budgets) became meaningless as money lost its value by the hour. Worse, lifetime savings vanished overnight, while economic life was reduced to barter."

(Great Britain rcognized that without Germany's recovery, there would be little hope of a return to Europe's prewar prosperity.)

Note: in the following table on page 204 the column headed Summer 1923 shows a rapid decline at the time the brothers departed.

Entwicklung der Preise in Deutschland in Deutsch-Mark.
(Evolution of Prices in Germany in Marks)

	before 1914	1918	1922	Sommer 1923	November 1923
1 pound of potatoes	0,04*	0,12	80M	2.000M	50.0 Milliarden**
1 egg	0,08	0,25	180M	5.000M	80.0 Milliarden
1 glass of beer	0,13	0,17	60M	3.000M	150.0 Milliarden
1 pound of meat	0,90	2,00M	1200M	90.000M	3.2 Billionen
1 pound of butter	1,40	3,00M	2400M	150.000M	6.0 Billionen

*As already presented, the punctuation is according to the European system, decimal and comma reversed. Therefore, 0,04 means four cents, but not an American four cents, rather four pennies of a Mark (M).

**The Milliard is a denomination between the German Million and the German Billion. In other words, the Milliard equals an American billion. A German billion is an American trillion. The plural is formed by adding -en. The lowest rate of exchange in November 1923 was 4.2 trillion Marks to the dollar.

Price table courtesy Gerhard Rauscher, professor *emeritus* of German, Department of Foreign Languages, University of Wisconsin-Milwaukee.

15. KFR, 660-661. "When Germany early in January, 1923, was declared in default on deliveries of timber and coal, French and Belgian divisions marched into the Ruhr and occupied the industrial cities. The Ruhr occupation lasted until July, 1925 [or a year and a half], and called forth strong protests on the part of the British. The attempt made by France to exploit the rich industrial assets of the Ruhr District was, however, hampered by a German policy of passive resistance and non-co-operation, as decreed by the German government on January 19. Germany's plight aroused increasing sympathy in the United States and Great Britain, and a *démarche* in Paris was undertaken by the Vatican. Thus France found herself not only in a partial economic stalemate but also in a diplomatic situation which became more and more untenable."

16. **KFR 658-659.** Walter Rathenau, a member of the Wirth cabinet, was "the son of Emil Rathenau, the actual president of AEG (*Allgemeine Elektrizitätsgesellschaft*) [General Electric Company] a prominent industrialist, an economic expert of more than average capacity, and a sincere believer in international understanding. . . " The son "fell as the second victim of the *Organisation Konsul*. The assassins, when brought to trial, not only maintained that Rathenau deserved death as a Jew and an *Erfüllungspolitiker*, but they cynically confessed that the execution of the 'death sentence' had been necessitated by the very fact that a continuation of Rathenau's foreign policy would have proven advantageous to Germany and would thus have strengthened the prestige of the Weimar Republic."

17. **KFR 644.** In the ten months after the Germans had signed the Versailles Treaty, 750,000 German civilians lost their lives from malnutrition. KFR 653. "The food blockade was not terminated until July 12, 1919. On May 7 of that year Count von Brockdorff-Rantzau had indignantly referred to this fact in addressing the Versailles assembly. 'The hundreds of thousands of non-combatants . . . who have perished since November 11, 1918, as a result of the blockade, were killed with cold deliberation, after our enemies had been assured of their complete victory.'"

18. Frederick the Great of Prussia is known for having brought the potato from the inca terraces in South America to become a staple for his people.

19. The city, Konstanz, and Lake Constance—called the *Bodensee* in German—were named after Constantine, a Roman emperor who reigned in the third century. Germany, Austria and Switzerland share the lake's shoreline. See map "The Bodensee (Lake Constance)," *Germany*, Fodor's 2000, p. 220.

20. Religious reformer *Jan Hus* (John Huss) was tried for heresy in the fifteenth century in the *Konzilgebäude* (Council Building) in Konstanz before the Reform Council. Despite the fact that he was given *Freies Geleit* (safe conduct), in the end he was burned at the

stake in 1415. A century later Martin Luther fared better, being allowed his freedom after his heresy trial in Worms. *Germany*, Insight Guides, 1998, p. 208 (See also *Germany*, Fodor's 2000, "Bodensee," p. 227)

21. On pages 11, 19-23, and 78-79 in Reeves, Pamela, *Ellis Island*, you will find references to steerage. By the time Theodor and Adolf traveled in 1923, steerage tickets were called third-class.

22. "*Pfingstrosen*" (peonies) are literally Pentecost roses, because they bloom around Pentecost at the end of May. Pentecost Monday is a holiday in Germany.

23. *Meister:* master craftsmen usually have their own premises and are entitled to accept apprentices who want to learn their trade.

24. The younger generation of Ritsches did not carry on the large family pattern. They married later and had fewer children. With the exception of the oldest Josef, who married at the age of 23, and one who never married, three married in their late twenties (one was the author's father, Theodor at 29), five married in their early thirties, two in their late thirties, and one in his early forties. Of the married, three had no children, six had one or two children, two had four children, one had six, and one (the author's father) had seven.

25. *Geselle:* The second step in the trade learning sequence, a journeyman, usually travels stopping at locations where he can gain the experience practicing his trade under additional masters.

26. *Schwabenland* is in the southwest corner of Germany, roughly compatible with the state of Baden-Württemberg. It reaches in the south to Lake Constance, which is sometimes called the "Swabian Sea." In the far southwest corner of Swabia lies the Black Forest (*der Schwarzwald*), in which the evergreens are so dense that they project a black cast when seen from a distance.

27. KFR 602. The chronological legislative enactment is as follows: "health insurance (1883); accident insurance (1884-1887); old age and disability insurance (1889)." See KFR 617 for

description of events.

28. The city of *Meersburg am Bodensee*, "is considered to be one of the best-preserved medieval towns in Germany. The magic of the place is best appreciated in the evening . . . Time then to admire the half-timbered houses . . . The historical centre is marked by the Old Castle, [*die Meersburg*] one of the oldest in Germany dating from Merovingian times. In the New Castle, the erstwhile summer residence of the prince-bishops of Konstanz, classical concerts are now performed." *Germany*, Insight Guides, 1998, p. 209 (See also *Germany*, Fodor's 2000, p., 227-229.)

29. To wish someone luck (*Glück*), Germans press their thumbs for someone, rather than crossing their fingers.

30. In his booklet *Die Meersburg*, (here the fortified castle) Verlag Schnell-Steiner, München/Zurich, 1984, Hubert Naessl reports two unusual facts: a) in the early days [seventh century] a well was bored through solid rock in the enclosed garden of the Castle; b) at one time the Castle defaulted to the Diocese in Konstanz across Lake Constance from Meersburg, because the current noble had no heirs.

31. Care has been taken to use most German nouns in nominative case in the text, so that the non-German reader is not confused by different case endings.

32. The Dagobert Tower was named after a king in the Merovingian dynasty which immediately preceded the Carolingian dynasty which *Charlemagne* (or Charles the Great, *Karl der Große*) began in the eighth century.

33. Annette von Droste-Hülshoff is considered among Germany's finest poets, some say its finest woman poet. She lived on occasion in the Old Castle, owing to the generosity of her uncle, who had ownership at the time. The richness of her apartments is well-maintained, as well as is the armor, dating from the seventh century on.

34. Visitors can view the fortified castle (die Burg) in part, including the poetess's apartment and the armor and can dine in its restaurant in season. Meersburgers affectionately call it the Old Castle, or "das Alte Schloß" to contrast with the New Castle, built a millennium later. A Schloß is usually more a luxurious residential palace, built after fortresses were no longer deemed necessary.

35. Droste-Hülshoff, Annette von, Sämtliche Werke, "Das Alte Schloß." Carl Hauser Verlag, 102 München, (1847?), p. 125. Originally the stanza printed here was from the Meersburger Balladen, 1841-42, stanza 1 of 5.

36. English translation by Marita E. Ritsche.

37. Over a millennium younger than das Alte Schloß, das Neue Schloß, (also called the "Barockschloß," because of its baroque style), was designed in part by Balthasar Neumann, Germany's leading architect of the eighteenth century. It was built as a residence for the bishops of Konstanz. Today concerts take place in the glittering Spiegelsaal (Hall of Mirrors) The top floor houses the Dornier Museum on German aircraft. See also Fodor's Germany, 2000, p. 227-228.

38. Ringstraßen (ring streets) mark where a fortified wall once stood. When removed, in its place a street is built. It encloses or encircles the "inner city,"often called die Altstadt, the Old City.

39. The products named "4711" are associated with city of Cologne (Köln). The perfume derives its name from the street number, "4711," of the factory on the Glockergasse. Germany, Fodor's, 2000, p. 405.

40. In the field of cookery Dr. Oetker carries the same prestige in Germany as Ann Pillsbury or Betty Crocker in America.

41. The Norddeutscher Lloyd steamship company was founded in Bremerhaven in 1861 the year that the North German Confederation was formed under Prussia's leadership. Ten years later the southern states joined the confederation to become the Second Reich.

42. *Hannover* in German is spelled with two n's. It is also stressed differently: Hahn-NO-ver, whereas in English it is usually HAH-no-ver.

43. The Ruhr region today is one of the wealthiest districts in Germany. For a modern description see *Germany*, Fodor's 2000, "The Rhineland," 408-411.

44. KFR 660-661. "In the meantime, the disintegration of the German currency had become catastrophic. The German government had promised to reimburse German industrialists in the Ruhr for forced reparations deliveries and to compensate idle workers for the loss in wages. The printing presses worked overtime to turn out immense quantities of paper money without gold coverage, and soon Germany found herself engulfed in a mad whirlpool of uncontrolled inflation. Before long the equivalent of the dollar was quoted in millions and billions of paper marks. The speed with which the inflation proceeded was such that employees and wage earners had to be paid daily to allow them to catch up with the runaway prices. Even so, the fantastic amounts of paper earnings received became worthless within a few hours.

"But what was a nightmare for the average German citizen turned out to be a field day for the holders of foreign currency. The country found itself overrun with foreigners who bought up commodities in such quantities and at such a rate that most stores were completely sold out in the early morning hours, and were unable to replenish their stocks. The German and non-German holder of foreign currency could purchase industrial plants, ancient castles, land, and real estate for a mere trifle. Savings, insurance policies and pensions were invalidated, and the entire German middle class was reduced to penury. Resentment against the *nouveaux riches* and ill feeling against foreigners were on the increase, and a wave of anti-Semitism swept over the country. The economic chaos proved a fertile breeding ground for cynicism, moral license, and political radicalism."

45. KFR 716. Käthe Kollwitz' sketches in charcoal were an appropriate medium to depict the dreary post Great War (World War I) era. "A member of the socialist party and animated by a deep sympathy with proletarian misery, this woman dedicated her great artistic talent to the single task of a passionate indictment of social injustice. In some of her etchings, as, for example, in the dramatic scenes depicting the uprising of the Silesian weavers [the craftsmen were victims of the industrial revolution], [she] rose above any partisan creed to a timeless symbolization of human suffering."

46. The standard language, that is, that which is taught in school, used in the news media and in formal social situations is High, or better, Standard German. It stands in opposition to dialects which are supposedly mutually intelligible variations within a language. Native speakers, however, will maintain that they from time to time cannot understand a compatriot's dialect from another area. Since dialects developed at a time when barriers to mobility, and thus communication, were limited by geographical formations, such as mountains or waterways, one would find that an overlay of a linguistics map over a topographical map would closely coincide. See further # 48.

47. *Germany*, Insight Guides, 1998, p. 209, *Germany*, Fodor's 2000, pp. 225-226. The Zeppelin factory, in Friederichshafen on the shore of Lake Constance, played a central part in Germany's aeronautic history. It included the development of the zeppelin airship, named after its inventor Graf (Count) Ferdinand von Zeppelin, before World War I and the Dornier seaplanes. The former was launched from a floating hangar on the lake whereas the latter were tested on its water's surface. The Hindenburg, which caught fire at a show in New Jersey, is probably the most notorious of the Zeppelin "airships.".

48. Actually, in Germany three major dialect areas (containing innumerable minor variations within each) stretch across the map horizontally, roughly corresponding to the altitude of the land.

Thus, we have Low German spoken in the lowlands on the coast, with a dip southward along the Rhine valley, Middle German spoken in the midlands, and Upper German spoken in Alpine areas. Dialects may be used in dramatic productions to provide local color. Some persons, in speaking Standard German, nevertheless, have a pronunciation heavily flavored with their local dialect.

The Upper, and to a certain extent the Middle dialects, underwent a consonantal sound shift around the fifth century, according to Waterman below, although some put the shift in the eighth or ninth century, a phenomenon in which Low German did not participate. Thus English, which also did not experience a sound shift, can under certain conditions result in pronunciations more similar to the Low German dialects than to the Upper German dialects. The particular sounds concerned are p t k — pf ts(z) kx; examples are apple — Apfel, sit — sitzen, make — machen. For more detailed information, see Waterman, John T., *A History of the German Language,* University of Washington Press, Seattle, 1976, "The High German Sound Shift," p. 56-57.

It should be emphasized that Low German, though not an official language in Germany, is not a substandard form of German, as is popularly accepted. It would be better to call it Lower or Lowland German, one of three major dialectical families spoken in opposition to Standard German, depending on one's location. Moreover, Low German distinguished itself for being the *lingua franca* of the North and Baltic Seas for those countries that participated in the Hanseatic League. Dutch, a form of Low German, is the official language of the Netherlands. Don Zamzow, Interview May 25, 2004.

49. Those in the lowlands, especially those in former Pommern, now Poland, term the general dialect *Plattdeutsch,* a spelling variation thereof, or simply *Platt* (in English — "flat/low" referring here to the topography). In Standard German it is called *Plattdeutsch.*

Part Two: Across the Big Pond

50. For more information on Atlantic crossing activities in the nine-teenth and early twentieth centuries, see Levine, Ellen, *If Your Name Was Changed at Ellis Island*, Scholastic, NY, 1993. Her delightful book for children about America's immigrants would entertain even some adults with certain of its information.

51. *Struwwelpeter* is a storybook character who never cuts his hair or his fingernails.

52. Today such city states are honored by putting an H before the city's initial on car plates, as in HB, Hansastadt Bremen or HH, Hansastadt Hamburg. For further reading on the Hanseatic League, consult KFR, *Germany: 2000 Years*, v. I, "The Rise and Fall of the Holy Roman Empire," Frederick Ungar Publishing, N.Y., 1969, p.119-120.

53. KFR 658-659. "On May 11, 1921, the Wirth government [under the Weimar Republic] accepted the London ultimatum, and Germany, aside from her continued deliveries in kind [that is, cattle, equipment, and chemical products] to France, paid a first reparations installment of one hundred and fifty million gold marks. Both Wirth and [Walter] Rathenau [signers] were hence-forth denounced by their domestic foes as the inaugurators of the German *Erfüllungspolitik* (fulfillments policy). Resentment against all those responsible for the signing of the Versailles Treaty reached a high pitch." There ensued a series of murders "by members of the secret military *Organisation Konsul*" . . . " [one of] the gradually emerging forces of counterrevolution and rightist reaction."

54. *Two Hundred Years of German-American Relations 1776-1976: A Documentary*, Heinz Moos Verlag, München, Thomas Piltz, ed.,(a bilingual book in English and German), 1975. "Steerage, located between hold and deck, space without air or light, ceiling 5 1/2' high; adult 18" space, child 1/2 that." For other ship conditions, see also Levine, *If Your Name Was Changed*, p. 25-26.

55. *Underberg* is one of two well-known brands of stomach tonic, *Jägermeister* being the other. They have uses similar to that of Angostura bitters. Among the ingredients is the gentian plant, a blue flower that grows in the Alps. Up to four teaspoons of the tonic taken alone can be used as a stomach calmative, taken after meals it acts against flatulence. As imbibers know, a dash of bitters is used in many alcoholic drinks and informed cooks may use it to flavor soups and the like.

56. Grant, Sue, *German Life*, December 2002 – January 2003, "100 Years-Steiff Teddy Bears," pp.38-39. Margarete Steiff, a wheelchair entrepreneur, began her plush toy company in 1877. It expanded rapidly. Her nephew had a hand in developing it, especially the toy bear about the time of the "Teddy's Bear incident" in America when President Theodore Roosevelt on a hunting expedition refused to shoot a tied-up bear. In Germany the figure is called accordingly the Teddy bear. As it says in the article, "He is at home anywhere, but holds dual American and German nationality." Steiff toys are distinguished by a metal button fastened to the toy's ear *(Knopf im Ohr)*.

57. A *Stammtisch* is a table reserved for regular guests in a local restaurant.

58. The Fuggers,(as well as the Welsers), were wealthy bankers with branches in the Americas.

59. Wind and weather and their related health concerns are discussed in Levine's children's book, *If Your Name Was Changed*, p. 24-28.

60. Goethe, Johann Wolfgang von, *Deutsche Gedichte*, Echtermeyer, revision Benno von Wiese, August Basel Verlag, Duisberg, 1956, "*Gesang der Geister über den Wassern*," p. 198. *The Penguin Book of Verse*, Leonard Forster, ed., 1965, p. xiv, notes that Goethe "was the first writer in German since Luther whose work compelled the attention of a European public . . . His guiding principle that all being was an organic whole informs his poetry and ensures a basic

strictness of form despite apparent irregularities . . . the 'Olympian serenity' of his later work was achieved only by a balance of opposing forces . . ."

61. English translation by Marita E. Ritsche. *The Penguin Book of Verse*, Leonard Forster, ed., p. 210, also has a translation but no attempt was made to preserve the style of the poem.

62. *Karl der Große*, or in America known as *Charlemagne*, founded what has come to be called the Holy Roman Empire. He thought to join political with religious forces by having himself crowned in Rome by the Pope. Thus over time the empire's name, according to some, came to imply the following: Holy (papal crowning), Roman (took place in Rome) Empire (a vast amount of land). Nevertheless, the common interpretation is that this First Reich was neither Holy (had its own forms of corruption) nor Roman (its rulers were Germanic, later German) nor Empire (in reality a loose decentralized confederation of German kingdoms). Its focus was dependent on the current dynasty in power. Nor did the Empire have a single capital over the years, but rather a range of cities from Aachen, Prague, and Vienna. Nonetheless, its rule covered a thousand years, if one counts its inception with the coronation in Rome of *Karl des Großen* in 800 AD and its termination with the succumbing of the Hapsburg dynasty to Napoleonic troops in 1806. Thereby comes the third term sometimes ascribed to it, namely the Thousand Year Reich. Added to the title in 962 were the words "of the German Nation."

63. The name Koblenz comes from the Latin "Confluence," or "flowing together." The area is also called "*das Deutsche Eck,*" because of the "corner of land" that juts into the Rhine juncture.

64. The many onion-towered church steeples (*Zwiebeltürme*) in southern Germany are an influence of Byzantine architecture.

65. Solinger: one of the famous brands of steelware, this from Solingen; Rosenthal: probably the best-known of the many German porcelain brands in Bavaria.

66. As is true with most of Europe, America often applies a regional custom as if it were a national phenomenon, ignoring that Europe came of age before technology, and thus mobility, which would hinder regional customs from finding national acceptance.

67. Traditionally women were to devote their efforts to *Kinder, Küche, und Kirche* (children, kitchen and church).

68. Many such regional handicrafts first spread throughout the nation after the Great War.

69. For information on Meißen porcelain, see *Germany*, Insight Guides, 1998, "From Berlin to Dresden," p.145-6, or for the origins of porcelain, see *Germany*, Fodor's 2000, pp. 579-581.

70. *www.ellisisland.org*. A third-class ticket cost fifteen dollars which seems a small amount to us today. However, one must remember that daily life for poorer people did not usually include handling money. First-class tickets were $45 and second-class $25 in the early 1900s.

71. The lack of cohesiveness in the Holy Roman Empire gradually became a detriment to Germany as other countries with far less territory surpassed its political development. The lack of an ongoing capital also supports the theory of weaker political strength. The founding dates of national capitals are, of course, obscure, but the following statistics are given by the *Encyclopedia Britannica*, Madrid (1047); London (597) but known in Roman times; Paris is at least 2000 years old; Moscow, first mentioned in 1147; Berlin (1244), but had no national, let alone international, prestige until 1871, as capital of the Second Reich. Aside: *Encyclopedia*, v. 2, p. 849, says mid-twentieth century Berlin was "a city divided by a wall more appropriate to the Middle Ages."

72 The reader will remember that Denmark, Portugal, and the Netherlands, with their maritime prowess, also took part in the quest for overseas colonies. KFR 166. For a time the Holy Roman Emperor Charles V, inheriting some lands of the Spanish throne,

even possessed Spanish territories in the New World, but that endured only a short time.

73. KFR 306-307. "*Louis XIV and the German Empire.*" The French had their eye on the left bank of the Rhine almost since the time of Charlemagne, but in the eighteenth century Louis XIV, conscious of the strength of his position and well aware of the inherent weakness of the Empire, carried out a comprehensive program of national aggrandizement at German expense. His designs aimed at the realization of what he called France's 'natural frontiers,' meaning the acquisition of all of Alsace and most of the other territories on the left bank of the Rhine. . . . including the Rhenish Palatinate, the Spanish Netherlands, and part of the Dutch Republic. . . . Feeling himself to be the heir of Charlemagne, he dreamed of disinheriting the Hapsburgs and of resurrecting a Frankish Empire under French leadership. In this grandiose political scheme the river Rhine was to become the natural and national boundary of France . . . he could count on the sympathy and support of most of the German princes, and also the aid of Sweden, which owed her position as a great power to French intervention . . . "the anti-imperial sentiment in Poland and the Franco-Turkish alliance forged the remaining links in the combination of powers which encircled the German Empire on all sides."

KFR 323. "The Aims of French Aggression. We recall that it had always been Louis XIV's great ambition to overthrow the dominion of the Hapsburg emperors, to gain possession of the left bank of the Rhine, and to subject the German states to French supremacy. It would have been the crowning achievement of his life if all these designs had finally converged in the resurrection of the Empire of Charlemagne."

74. KFR 450. "Napoleon and the New Military Strategy. In the age of Absolutism and Enlightened Despotism the armies had been the exclusive creation and property of the rulers . . . the strategy of . . .

the absolutistic princes were artistically conceived chess games that aimed less at the destruction than at the paralyzation of the enemy . . . the new methods were perfected by the generals of the French Revolution and especially by the greatest of them, Napoleon Bonaparte . . . the masses of citizen armies acquired a new significance in defense and attack . . . and were inspired by the ideals of personal devotion to a common cause . . . The result was a new military strategy that aimed at the annihilation of the enemy, achieved by the force of superior numbers and by a relentless offensive initiative that dictated the law of action to the opposing armies."

75. KFR 400. Napoleon "tried to revive Roman imperialism in a Christian garb, visited the tomb of Charlemagne at Aix-la-Chapelle [Aachen], and crowned himself emperor in the presence of the pope." During this period of French imperialism, however, Napoleon stretched far beyond the borders of the Holy Roman Empire, attempting a westward expansion into Spain (Goya's "The Executions," immortalizes the French invasion), and an eastward extension as far as Russia (immortalized in Tschaikovsky's "Overture to the War of 1812").

76. KFR 510-511. The German Confederation, arising as a protectorate under Napoleon after the fall of the Holy Roman Empire in 1806, consisted of innumerable German principalities, each insisting on its own sovereignty and glorification. The princes vied with each other for pomp and power rather than devoting their energies toward unification. It was "not yet a nation in the same sense in which France, England, or Russia were sovereign and relatively homogeneous states . . . The fifty years that followed the passage of the 'Act of Confederation' witnessed various attempts on the part of the German people to break the political deadlock that was preventing Germany from reaching the goal of her national aspirations." See also KFR 456.

77. It may be that no European country has sustained the regular draining of strategic non-conventional thinkers as has Germany from the pietists of the seventeenth century, who rejected the conventional religious ways; to the Revolutionaries of 1848, who fled for their lives when their assembly failed; to those artists, musicians, poets, dramatists, novelists, and filmmakers who fled Nazi persecution after 1933 so they could practice their creative talents in a free environment; to the scientists who were garnered for the American space program after1945.

78. KFR 553-554. A series of inventions in telegraphy finally enabled Werner von Siemens "to become the leading electro-technical industrialist in Europe . . . The most impressive accomplishments of the German iron and steel industries are associated with the family Krupp." The goal was to manufacture a type of cast steel, equal or better than that of England. But traditionally German economic development, like its political development, had lagged behind that of other European countries. The Italian Antonio Genovesi had predicted in 1765 "that the productive capacity of German trade and commerce would never equal that of France and England," a theory upon which the major European countries may have relied. The turn of status in European affairs, that this up-to-now backward German nation was making great strides in fields other than government, especially threatened the major powers.

79. KFR 542-545. It was the first unification of German states since the fall of the Holy Roman Empire over fifty years before. "Prussia's military victories and Bismarck's diplomatic successes at home and abroad had been viewed with growing apprehension by France. Ever since the time of Richelieu it had been one of the aims of French politicians to prevent the rise of a strong and united empire across the Rhine." Early on Napoleon III steered clear of interfering with Prussian foreign politics in the hopes of territorial gains later on, "specifically part of the left bank of the Rhine, including

the city of Mainz . . . " Moreover, he was busy trying to establish "a Mexican empire under French protection, to be headed by Archduke Maximilian of Austria." The United States, just emerging from their Civil War, declared France in "flagrant violation of the Monroe Doctrine. France withdrew her troops, and Archduke Maximilian was shot by Mexican insurgents."

80. KFR 542-545. In the late nineteenth century, when Napoleon III then demanded the German left bank, he thought he would have the support of the south German states. Meantime, however, Bismarck had shrewdly made secret alliances with them and furthermore counted on the neutrality of European allies in case of war. Bismarck adulterated political messages between the two countries, which cast aspersions on France. In the end "Napoleon faced a united Germany whose peoples had forgotten all their political, social, and tribal differences. Almost overnight it had acquired a national will and a national physiognomy," which contributed to its victory in the Franco-Prussian War in 1871.

The motivation behind Hugo von Hofmannsthal's composition, "*Deutschland über Alles*," which became the national anthem, was also national unity. Composed about this time "Germany Above All" was not implying expansionist aims, but rather was praising the German principalities, which had at last seen fit to unite their many regions under a national umbrella. Considering the laborious, drawn-out struggle, it is unlikely that the Germans were planning on an imminent extension of borders. It took some forty years before the song was misappropriated.

81. KFR 605-608. "The new German Empire, a latecomer among the great powers of Europe, was built on the national unity achieved in 1871, and its citizens, on the whole, accepted cheerfully Bismarck's 'Small-Germany' solution [minus Austria] of the German Question." There were, however, dissenting groups, and one of their spokesmen was Konstantin Frantz . . . He was an astute political thinker and an uncompromising antagonist of

Bismarck, who had advocated in his writings the idea of a federated 'Greater Germany' [including Austria] which was to become the nucleus of a future world federation."

82. KFR 630. "<u>Germany As a World Power</u>. The boom of 1871 and the crash of 1873 were followed by a speedy stabilization of German economy, a process in which the skillful exploitation of natural resources played a conspicuous part."

83. KFR 553-554. But by the middle of the nineteenth century, "Germany began to comprehend realistically the new problems presented by the Industrial Revolution," [and] "she pushed ahead with typical German thoroughness and tenacity. Germany was rich in ore and coal deposits and her people had learned discipline of thought and work in the schools and in the army. These acquired habits were complemented by an inborn talent for organization and administration."

84. KFR 607. "<u>Bismark's Foreign Policy (after 1871)</u>. William I, the new German emperor, and his trusted chancellor who had built the strongest nation on the European continent, found themselves immediately confronted with the task of allaying foreign apprehensions as to the future policies of Germany and therefore of convincing their neighbors that they had nothing to fear from a united and prosperous German nation. 'We are satiated,' declared Bismarck shortly after the Peace of Frankfurt [the settlement after the Franco-Prussian War 1870-1871]. 'It has always been my aim,' he added, 'to win the confidence of Europe and to convince it that German policy will be just and peaceful, now that it has repaired the *injuria temporum*, the disintegration of the nation.'*" [*referring to the Holy Roman Empire of the German Nation] Still there were many dangerous tensions. "It required the skill of a great statesman to neutralize these antagonistic forces and to steer the ship of State safely through many a threatening storm."

85. KFR 632. "The fact that Germany's manufacturing output more than trebled and her national income doubled during the reign of

William II is in part at least attributable to this form of rationalized or 'planned' capitalism."

86. KFR 625. "Colonial Frictions and International Crises. In the period from 1871 to 1895, the proportion of the rapidly growing German population to the available domestic resources was most unfavorable. Colonial expansion could thus be justified on economic grounds partly from the need for new markets which were not closed by foreign protective tariffs and partly from the desire to find outlets for the surplus population of the homeland. The stabilization of German economy during the final years of the nineteenth century, however, invalidated the force of these arguments. England in particular viewed with growing suspicion the renewed 'German demands for additional colonies.' In her own case she regarded the possession of a colonial empire and the command of an adequate sea power for its protection as a matter of life or death, whereas in the case of Germany she recognized no such necessity and therefore interpreted the German demands as a deliberate challenge to the British empire. It is thus hardly surprising that international crises multiplied after 1895, many growing out of the rival colonial ambitions of Europe's great powers. And though many of these incidents were disposed of by arbitration or some compromise solution, each of them left a residue of bitterness and distrust which tended to heighten the tenseness of the international situation."

87. KFR 617. "From his uncle, Frederick William IV, the new emperor had inherited the idea of the 'divine right' and mission of kings and princes, but a lack of real self-assurance due to inexperience made him feel outweighed and overshadowed by Bismarck's genius. The desire for self-assertion and for popular acclaim caused him to bluster and blunder. Nevertheless, it seemed at first that William II was willing to fall in line with Bismarck's established policies." But hope for working with the European community was not to last.

88. The *K. and K. Zeit* is an abbreviation for *Die kaiserliche und königliche Zeit*—the era of czars and kings.

89. KFR 617-618. Bismarck knew to court England's favor. But in 1888 Prince Wilhelm of Prussia became German emperor and king of Prussia. The relationship between this young Kaiser Wilhelm II and the experienced Bismarck came to a halt two years later, when the czar asked for Bismarck's resignation over Bismark's objection to the audience with cabinet members without his presence.

    The nobility of Great Britain and Germany were related through the family of Gotha-Saxe-Coburg, of the House of Hannover, Germany, land that England owned for a while. Kaiser Wilhelm II had been a much favored grandson of Queen Victoria of England, but ended by losing favor with his grandmother's nation due to his unilateral decisions, dictatorial manner, and uncompromising competitive spirit—he appeared to be upsetting the *status quo*. Later the British branch of the House of Gotha-Saxe-Coburg disowned the German part of its heritage by changing its name to the House of Windsor.

90. KFR 619. "Bismarck retired to his estate of Friedrichsruh near Hamburg which during the remaining years of his life became the object of veritable pilgrimages of men and women from many regions and lands and from all walks of life. The first and greatest chancellor of the Second German Empire died on July 30, 1898."

91. KFR 618-619. "In a document which summarized the issues that had brought on the crisis and specified the reasons for submitting his resignation, Bismarck once more stressed the necessity of continued friendly relations with Russia, as any other course 'would endanger all the important successes gained by the German Empire in the last decades under the rule of Your Majesty's two predecessors.'"

92. KFR 620-621. "The 'New Course' naval building program of [Admiral von] Tirpitz, which aimed at constructing a High Seas

Fleet second to none, was met across the Channel with the announcement that England would launch two warships for each German one . . . Although no formal treaty was as yet signed between the two powers [France and England], they were drawn together by the mutual sympathies of their [new] political leaders [Théophile Delcassé and King Edward VII] and as well by their common opposition to Germany's 'new course'." Further treaties were enacted "only after the German emperor [Wilhelm II] had consistently and obstinately refused to consider any limitation of the German fleet."

93. KFR 606. "Two Concepts of Empire. Friedrich Wilhelm Foerster, one of the most severe contemporary critics of the iron chancellor who, according to his own testimony, 'grew up in an atmosphere of loathing for Bismarck's work,' finds in the writing of Frantz support for this contention that 'autocracy superseded federation as the principle of unity. Force replaced the determination and establishment of law and legal rights. Bismarck thus founded that empire which Nietzsche denounced as the extirpation of the German spirit.' (Friedrich Wilhelm Foerster, Europe and the German Question, New York, Sheed and Ward, 1940, p. 20.) Because he excluded from his *Kleindeutschland* the Austrians and Sudeten Germans, Bismarck is for the Austrian historian Richard von Kralik 'not the creator but the destroyer of German unity.' The advocates of *Großdeutschland* maintained that Bismarck's Empire simply absorbed Germany into Prussia . . . and forced it into a dangerous and in the long run disastrous competition with the British empire."

94. KFR 315. By the late 1700s "the Prussian-Austrian dualism of interests and ambitions had come into the open and provided a keynote in the following struggle for national unity and the cultural integration of modern Germany . . . a most unfortunate result of the Prusso-Austrian rivalry in the eighteenth century was the ever growing influence of foreign powers in German politics. Austria, to gain the support of France and Russia, sacrificed

Spanish Netherlands (the territory of Belgium) to France, and East Prussia to Russia (Russian occupation, 1758-1768).

95. KFR 307-308. In the seventeenth century during the reign of Louis XIV in France, designs on the Rhineland threatened the German Empire: "All the odds seemed to be against the [German] Empire. If Louis had confined himself to his anti-imperial policies he might have succeeded in his far-reaching plans. However, the aspirations of French imperialism transcended Louis' continental European ambitions. In his attempt to extend French political and economic supremacy to the colonial possessions overseas he challenged the rival claims of Spain, England, and the Netherlands alike. Louis overreached himself and, though partly successful in his aggressive policies against the Empire, suffered ultimate defeat at the hands of the Great Powers of Europe . . . When Louis violated the terms of the Truce of Regensburg (1687), by a renewed attack on the Rhenish Palatinate [which is west of the Rhine], he found himself confronted not only by a suddenly aroused and united Germany but simultaneously by a European coalition of powers, headed by England . . . The Peace of Ryswik (1697) marked the end of the war against the Palatinate and brought humiliating terms for Louis . . . " At that time also "The Peace of Carlowitz (1699) made Hungary a part of Austria and raised the Austro-Hungarian monarchy to the rank of a Great Power."

96. Pan-Slav movements in the Austro-Hungarian Empire were strong in pre-World War I. KFR 633. "If Austria could conciliate the Serbs within her territory by becoming a federal, instead of a dual monarchy, Serbia could join such a federation . . . And since the other Balkan States would soon see the advantages gained from membership in the Austrian League of Nations, they might also join . . . The fact that none of the statesmen of modern Austria envisioned or attempted such a solution constitutes one of the tragic pages in the chapter of lost opportunities in the history of Austria and eastern Europe."

97. KFR 630. "Germany As a World Power. Several motivating forces, some of them inherent in the national character, others attributable to historical and geographical circumstances, contributed to the phenomenal growth of the new German empire to a dominant position in Europe and in the world." . . . "But the construction of the imposing edifice of German agriculture, industry, and commerce required not only personal initiative and careful planning but even more a talent for large-scale organization and the will to unselfish and disciplined individual and collective action. A country with a soil of less than average fertility and an extremely narrow seaboard could overcome such handicaps only by superb teamwork and a rigid rationalization of its economic forces and resources. It proved a great boon that German private enterprise was traditionally accustomed to accept directives from above. And the fact these directives were given by industrial and economic experts of more than average intelligence accounts in no small measure for the German success to take long-range views and not to shun major risks in providing the necessary credits . . . " [termed *die Gründerzeit* — the founding years]

98. KFR 608. As the new empire [Second Reich] " . . . consolidated politically and economically by the decisive victory over France (Franco-Prussian War 1870-1871), [along with] the prompt payment of the French indemnity, and the ensuing expansion of industry, trade, and commerce–rapidly advanced to a leading and pivotal position in Europe, the people found little reason to quarrel with Bismarck or to question the wisdom of his political course. If Bismarck was guilty of nationalism, he shared this guilt with his age: nationalism was in its ascendancy everywhere . . . " Bismarck felt the tension among the great powers, especially of France, its "Frankish sibling." [Germany's name for France is *Frankreich*, "the Frankish Kingdom," the Franks being a Germanic tribe within France's ancestry.] "To isolate France and frustrate her

desire for revenge, the German chancellor built a system of defensive alliances with Austria, Russia and Italy. (*Dreikaiserbund*—the Three Emperors' League.)" The chapter goes on to describe the intricacies of power, tension, and jealousy among the European nations. See pp. 609ff.

99. KFR 632-636. Germany had come to the aid of its central power, Austria, when the Archduke, heir to the throne in Austria-Hungary, was assassinated in Sarajavo, a Bosnian town. Their ally Italy declared neutrality in the beginning, but Turkey decided to join them. Japan went to the side of the Allies. "The German people—not differing greatly in this respect from the populations in the enemy countries—were familiar only with the surface phenomena . . . were therefore convinced that Germany had become the victim of a dastardly international plot and that the very existence of the 'encircled' fatherland was at stake."

100. KFR 642. "During September and October [1918] Bulgaria and Turkey collapsed, and the Austrian empire was in a process of rapid disintegration. On November 4 the Dual Monarchy capitulated, Emperor Charles abdicated, and the Polish, Czech, Croat, and Slovene minorities rose in revolt and declared their autonomy." KFR 649. "The incorporation of German Austria in the federal organism of the *Reich* was envisaged by Article 2 of the Weimar Constitution, and Article 61 provided for Austrian representation in the *Reichsrat* in a consultative capacity. As early as November 12, 1918, the Austrian national assembly had endorsed Article 1 of an Austrian Provisional Constitution, stating that 'German Austria is a constitutent part of the German Republic.' Plebiscites held in several regions of German Austria gave evidence of overwhelming sentiment in favor of an *Anschluß*, [annexation] for both at the time and in later years, the realization of this common aspiration of the advocates of *Großdeutschland* [Germany plus Austria] was prevented by the uncompromising opposition of the Allies."

101. KFR 642-644. Wilson's 14 Points (January1918) proposed a basis for peace. "The one consolation of the German people in their defeat and misfortune lay in their hope for a new era of political democracy and both social and international justice. Such a new era seemed to be reasonably assured by the German acceptance of President Wilson's 'Fourteen Points' and by the willingness of the German people to atone for the sins of their political and military leaders. It was this hope and this implicit trust in a saner and juster world order which acted as a moderating influence on the forces of revolution and eventually determined the triumph of constitutional government over leftist radicalism. Despite their many miseries and heartaches the Germans now breathed under a freer sky than they had for many decades, and they took a certain pride in putting their own house in order and in firmly resolving to gain back the confidence of the world."

102. KFR 639. " . . . the German government had extended some peace feelers, chiefly to induce the allied powers to make public their war aims. Yet these German overtures of December, 1916, were rejected by the Allies on the ground that they impressed them as 'empty and insincere' and only intended to sow seeds of discord in their camp. The German peace initiative almost coincided with President Wilson's first note to the belligerents, in which he asked them to state the objectives they were fighting for. The demand of the American president caused some embarrassment among the allied powers, owing to the fact that (as was revealed in January, 1918, in the New York *Evening Post*) in autumn, 1916, they had concluded some secret treaties whose terms provided for considerable annexations in the East and West, proposed acquisition of enemy territory which equaled if not exceeded in scope the Pan-German dreams of conquest."

103. KFR 644. The Great War "had involved more than thirty nations, large and small." German casualties amounted to one million six hundred thousand dead of a total eight million soldiers [over

twenty percent], over four million wounded and two hundred thousand missing of twenty million wounded or missing total . . . German national debt stood at one hundred and seventy-six billion gold marks (forty-four billion dollars)."

104. KFR 651-652. "<u>The Treaty of Versailles</u>. On May 28, [1919] the Germans submitted a set of counter-proposals and registered a vigorous protest against the violation of the Pre-Armistice Agreement as embodied in the 'Fourteen Points.' The answer of the Allies, termed their 'last word,' made some minor concessions and declared in case the Germans refused to accept the peace terms as they then stood, the [food] blockade would be continued and Allied troops would occupy the larger part of Germany. As the German High Command insisted that military resistance to invasion was out of the question, the German delegation finally yielded, and on June 22 the National Assembly, confronted with an Allied ultimatum with a time limit of twenty-four hours, accepted the Versailles Treaty against 138 opposing votes. The formal signing took place on June 28 in the same Hall of Mirrors of Versailles Castle where the German empire had been proclaimed on January 18, 1871. The severest and most ignominious clause of the treaty, and the one to which the vote of the National Assembly had taken specific exception, was contained in Article 231, which stated that Germany acknowledged her and her allies' responsibility for causing all the loss and damage to which the Allied and Associated governments and their citizens have been subjected as a consequence of the war imposed upon them by the Central Powers. The German peace envoys had with a heavy heart accepted a dictated peace rather than lay their defenseless country open to invasion and the destruction of its national sovereignty. For thus having squarely shouldered their responsibility as the chosen representatives of the German people they were, before many years had passed, denounced as *Novemberverbrecher* (November criminals) by the domestic enemies of the Weimar republic." In other words, the

German signing for total responsibility was a trade-off for non-invasion of their helpless land.

105. KFR 653. "By the end of November [1918] this difficult military operation [withdrawal of all troops in occupied territories within a time limit of a few weeks] was completed. The withdrawal and the ensuing demobilization had proceeded in good order and without any breach of military discipline. During the same period 5000 locomotives, an equal number of motor trucks, 150,000 freight cars, and immense quantities not only of war material but of farm equipment [and livestock], including horses (150,000) cattle (880,000), sows (15,000), sheep (897,000) and goats (25,000), had to be delivered to the Allies. These stipulations, too, were fulfilled."

106. KFR 644. The British [food] blockade,[which continued through winter and lasted ten months after the Armistice had been signed on November 9, 1918] moreover, "had caused increasing suffering among the civilian population of the Central Powers, and Germany alone counted about three quarters of a million deaths attributable to malnutrition." KFR 653. "The food blockade was not terminated until July 12, 1919. On May 7 of that year Count von Brockdorff-Rantzau had indignantly referred to this fact in addressing the Versailles assembly. 'The hundreds of thousands of non-combatants,' the German chief delegate had stated, 'who have perished since November 11, 1918, as a result of the blockade, were killed with cold deliberation, after our enemies had been assured of their complete victory.'"

107. Comparison of Stipulations in European Treaties (data KFR; table MER)

Treaty	Peace of Paris	Peace of Frankfurt	Treaty of Versailles
Date signed	1815	Jan. 28,1871	June 28, 1919
Parties	France vs. Allied Powers Austria, England, Prussia, Russia	France vs. Prussia (Franco-Prussion War)	(Central vs. Allied) Powers Germany vs. France, England Italy, United States
Main figures	Napoleon Bonaparte	Bismarck	Count von Brockdorff-Rantzau Clemenceau, Lloyd George, Vittorio Orlando, Wilson*
Territory	France retained that of 1872, including Alsace, (plus receiving Avignon, duchy of Savoy, county of Zweibrücken?)	Annexation of Alsace Lorraine, incorporated into Prussia's administration without plebiscite	One-twelfth lost colonies Alsace Lorraine > France Eupen, Malmédy > Belgium Saar under League 15 years Polish regions of Prussia surrendered
		Danzig > "free city" economic life strangled by competition from Polish city Gdynia Upper Silesia (predominantly German important industrial city divided with Poland despite plebiscite for Germany)	Memel, northernmost German city > Lithuania Schleswig > Denmark armed forces reduced war criminals named for trial
Food blockade lifted			July 12, 1919
Indemnity	None imposed (hope in restoration of Bourbon dynasty)	About one billion dollars accomplished in two years	Allied Reparation Commissn: 33-44 billion dollars
Reparations	None, but France temporarily eliminated from power politics	German occupation of French fortresses until indemnity paid	Unable to pay, ten-year struggle** French-Belgian invasion of Ruhr
Outcome	North German Confederation/Austrian Empire	Second Reich	Weimar-Republic

> Symbol denotes became, went to

* Prime ministers of Germany, France, England, Italy and the President of the USA respectively

* * "When reason finally began to prevail, it was too late, because the Weimar Republic was already in its death throes." (KFR 656)

108. KFR 656. "It may be asked in conclusion: what actually had become of Woodrow Wilson's 'Fourteen Points?' Six of them—relating to the evacuation and restoration of Belgium (VII); liberation of French territory and restoration of Alsace-Lorraine to France (VIII); autonomous development of the non-Germanic peoples of Austria-Hungary (X);self-determination of Romania, Serbia, and Montenegro (XI); creation of an independent Poland with access to the sea (XIII); creation of a general association of nations to afford 'mutual guarantees of political independence and territorial integrity to great and small states alike' (XIV)—were either wholly or partially realized.

The remaining eight points were either entirely discarded—(I) "open covenants, openly arrived at; (II) freedom of the seas; (III) removal of economic barriers; (V) a free, open-minded, and absolutely impartial adjustment of all colonial claims—or so modified that little of the original substance was left."

109. KFR 629. "Germany was the cradle of 'classical pacifism,' best documented in Immanuel Kant's tract Zum ewigen Frieden (On Eternal Peace) [1795: See KFR 374 for more details.] and conceived by him as 'a scientific and practical conquest of the international system of power through the creation of an international system of law.' That European concern existed in general about maintaining peace can be seen in the many phenomena dedicated to the subject: the London Peace Society (1816) and the one on the European continent in Geneva in 1830 were the earliest foundings; the first international peace congress was held at Brussels in 1848; the Geneva Convention of 1864 resulted in the International Red Cross adopting provisions for the humane treatment of wounded enemy soldiers and prisoners of war; the German version of a Friedensgesellschaft (peace society) was founded in Berlin in 1892, peace conferences of the Hague occurred in 1899 and 1907." None of the provisions seemed to prevail except the International Red Cross, which would become the clean-up crew after man-made destruction.

110. Mann, Heinrich, Der Untertan, (The Subject),1918. The author was a resident of Lübeck, a former Hansastadt, in the cold, tree-less, windy north coast. Even though Mann's opinions didn't appear in formal print until later, the author expressed concern long before the Great War's outbreak for the mindset overtaking Europe. Thomas Mann's brother focused his attention on the character of the common citizen. Heinrich was concerned more about the prevailing social structure during the early part of the century when the Wilhelminian era was getting into full swing, so he started a series called the Kaiser Trilogy, The last in the series was completed in 1925.

The second of the three works the *Untertan* was devoted to the bourgeois social life of the Wilhelminian era. When the father punishes the son, it is not clear whom the father is really intending to punish–the child or his own hateful attributes which he sees, though unconsciously, in his son. The parents' marital arrangement provides an outlet for mutual blame. If the son doesn't "turn out," the father can say it was due to the mother's softness, whereas she in turn can say she was only obeying his orders. Obsessed with the profit motive to the exclusion of regard for any who might be trampled in the process, Diederich's role as factory supervisor toward his laborers comes out as a kind of modern hierarchy all over again in which only a few live a life of comfort.

111. KFR 549. Progress was not without price, to which Marx, Engels, Nietzsche and many others had alluded. Eventually, it became clear that longtime-existing capitalism combined with industrialism was producing a new money aristocracy alongside a propertyless class of wage earners. "The labor-displacing machinery made for an increasing insecurity in the life of the workingman, for sharp and ruthless practices in the labor market, and the accompanying evils of unemployment and destitution." The destruction of the pride of the artisan along with wretched working conditions including long hours in airless buildings within drab surroundings reduced "human existence to a subhuman level."

112. *Daten deutscher Dichting,* Frenzel and Frenzel, ed., Deutscher Taschenbuch Verlag, Munich, 1972. Brothers Jakob and Wilhelm collected folk tales and started publishing them in 1812.

113. The *Abitur* is the final exam at the close of high school and gives the student the right to enter the university.

114. *Das Max und Moritz Buch,* original verse and drawings by Wilhelm Busch, adapted for high school/intermediate students with notes and exercises by ed. Werner Meier, National Textbook Company, Skokie, IL, 1972, *"Letzter Streich,"* the last of seven tricks, concerning their hilarious end. There is also a reference in *Two Hundred Years,* p.130-132, which mentions cartoonist Wilhelm Busch and reproduces "Last (and Seventh) Trick." The graphic arts came into fashion, especially as weeklies with "comic strips" satirizing humankind's weakness. The most well-known were the mischievous Max and Moritz, which later inspired the *Katzenjammer Kids* strip so popular in America.

115. Faden, Doris, *German Life,* Oc/Nv 00, "What's in a name?" p. 54-55: The saying in German is:*"Das ist so, wie der kleine Moritz es sich vorstellt,"* implying a person's simplistic interpretation of a complicated phenomenon.

Part Three: The New Country

116. Reeves, Pamela, *Ellis Island: Gateway to the American Dream,* Barnes & Noble, N.Y., 1998. p. 51. "As many as two percent of the newcomers were sent home again each year, without ever setting foot on American shores outside Ellis Island. One of five immigrants had to spend long, anxious days or weeks in detention or quarantine,"some merely waiting until they could be processed, others until officials were satisfied that they met all the requirements for admission.

117. Reeves, *Ellis Island,* p.19-21. "In the words of Charles Dickens, [voyage 1842] the steerage passengers' quarters below-deck were an appalling 'little world of poverty.'"

118. Reeves, *Ellis Island*, p. 59. "One of the most dreaded parts of the physical was the eye examination, in which doctors flipped up the eyelids of each immigrant with a buttonhook, a hairpin, or their fingers, searching for the common eye disease of the time, trachoma, which was common in southeastern Europe, but relatively unknown in North America . . . Trachoma could lead to blindness if not treated."

119. Reeves, *Ellis Island*, p. 60. The writer Sholom Aleichem notes at the beginning of his journey in Antwerp a family "who all were healthy, except their little girl who had bad eyes. The father wanted to stay with her, but couldn't because his ship ticket would be lost." *Letters from Rifka* by Karen Hesse, Puffin Books, 1992, is devoted to the story of a Russian Jewish girl whose parents travel on to America, while she remains in Brussels until her scalp heals from ringworm.

120. Reeves, *Ellis Island*, p. 60. "Immigrants who got past the medical inspectors continued down the line and next met a woman whose job it was to look for likely prostitutes."

121. Reeves, *Ellis Island*, p. 56. "Once on Ellis Island, the immigrants typically had many long waits, and the best they could hope for was a two-to-three-hour ordeal."

122. For more on how the dishonest took advantage of foreigners, see Reeves, *Ellis Island*, mainly Chapter Three: "The Great Hall Fire and the Era of Reform," p. 37ff.

123. Reeves, *Ellis Island*, Chapters Three, above, and Four: "Island of Hope, Island of Tears." Among those who worked especially to improve conditions for immigrants were Theodore Roosevelt, William Williams, and Fiorello LaGuardia.

124. "Litzers" translates as "runners," used in NY to mean con men. *Two Hundred Years*, p. 36.

125. Reeves, *Ellis Island*, p. 108. Instead of investing money toward the improvement of Ellis Island, "in 1921, Congress imposed the first

quota law on immigration, limiting the number of Europeans who could enter each year to 3 percent of the foreign-born people of that nationality living in the United States in 1910." See also p. 113.

126. Reeves, *Ellis Island*, p. 62-63. "Although the government provided interpreters to aid the immigrants, there was much confusion among them at the barrage of questions, especially about names. Inspectors had to decipher the immigrants' names from handwritten manifest sheets supplied by the ships . . . Helen Barth, who worked for the Hebrew Immigrant Aid Society . . . described how many people left their homes with one name and arrived in America with another."

127. *Two Hundred Years*, p. 59. These words on the Statue's base appear in the famous poem "Colossus" by Emma Lazarus.

128. See *Two Hundred Years*, p. 39, for sketch of the plan for the Statue of Liberty. Eduoard-René de Laboulaye, Sculptor Frederic August Bartholdi didn't make the deadline. It was almost ten years later that the statue, buffeted by storms over the Atlantic, arrived safely in the New York harbor.

129. Reeves, *Ellis Island*, p. 11. "Only the poor [that is, third class ticketholders] were required to undergo inspection at Ellis Island."

130. The "six-second medical exam" was carried out extensively at least until 1911. Reeves, *Ellis Island*, p. 57.

131. Levine, *If Your Name Was Changed*, p. 47. Immigrants must be fit to work, but cannot have a job lined up, lest they be accused of taking a citizen's livelihood from him.

132. In Reeves, *Ellis Island*, pp. 37ff., the reader will find explanations of contagious diseases and their abbreviations used at Ellis Island. 'SI', which occurs a few paragraphs later, actually refers to further legal questioning. Various types of quarantines are mentioned on several pages in Reeves, p. 32-33, 51, and 64-68. On p. 67 she reports an incident about the sheltered life of a girl from an isolated district in Europe, who probably had never been alone in a room

with a man. She must have been struck with horror as the medical doctor proceeded with a physical exam.

133. The highpoint of immigration occurred between 1880 and 1900, when nine million immigrants came, the largest in any twenty-year period, and three more million came in the next ten years, one million in 1907 alone. They were mostly farmers then, but after the Great War, they were mostly skilled labor. Ellis Island's peak years occurred in the early 1900s, when 5,000 to 10,000 immigrants were passing through the gates in one day. Other points of entry were Philadelphia, Boston, or Baltimore on the East Coast and some on the gulf ports in the south as well as some on the western coast. Earlier they came through Castle Garden, an old concert hall on the port, but soon it became too small. For more statistics, see Reeves, *Ellis Island,* Chapter Four, "Island of Hope, Island of Tears,"pp. 51-95. She also has basic tables of immigrant numbers by year and by national origin.

134. *Two Hundred Years*, p. 70. For the suspension bridge, first posts were sunk into the bottom of the channel, then the sides were hung from the posts with the cables already connected. They were turned by a special machine of the inventor.

135. *Two Hundred Years*, p. 70. Other examples concern the telegraph conceived by Werner von Siemens and made workable by David Hughes; Philipp Reis, who had the idea of the telephone, but Alexander Graham Bell made his version practical to buy; the idea of an incandescent lamp was described by Heinrich Goebel, but Thomas Edison completed the invention. Oskar von Miller—the founder of the German Museum of Science and Industry in Munich—so admired Edison that he crossed the Atlantic to meet him personally.

136. Mark Twain also wrote "That Awful German Language," a hilarious essay included in *A Tramp Abroad*, an account of Twain's European trip.

137. Two Hundred Years, p. 15. Germantown [now a suburb of Philadelphia,] was one of the earliest German settlements. William Penn established a colony dedicated to the idea of absolute religious tolerance. The Quakers were one of many sects which had suffered persecution in the Old World for deviating from traditional religious practice. In Pennsylvania they and others sought the freedom to pursue a "quiet, honest, and God-fearing life." Many other of the numerous pietistic sects, such as the Mennonites, Amish, Schwenkfeldians, "Dunkers," Moravians and Lambadists, emigrated from central Europe, including Germany, Switzerland and Czechoslovakia, seeking freedom from religious persecution in the Americas.

138. *Two Hundred Years*, p. 15. The date on which the ship docked in Philadelphia, October 6, 1683, is celebrated in some communities as German-American Day.

139. *Two Hundred Years*, p. 16. "As early as 1688, [Pastorius] composed the manifesto, thought to be the first condemning the institution of slavery in America."

140. The Pennsylvania Dutch are part of the pietistic movement which began in the seventeenth century in Europe. KFR 364-368. Reinhardt manages an admirable summary of the status of various religious approaches during that century. Too long to reproduce here, an attempt is made to bring out the salient points impacting the need to emigrate. "Luther and Melancthon . . . in order to safeguard the edifice of their church, had eventually to eliminate all mystical religious impulses, and thus rationalism finally prevailed in theology as in other fields. In the centuries that followed the Reformation a growing number of people, unable to find an outlet for their thwarted emotional life in the rigid forms of orthodox dogmatism, began to segregate and separate themselves from the official churches and to form small groups, sects, and conventicles, in which they tried to satisfy their spiritual yearnings. In the seventeenth century, these timid beginnings converged in

the movement which has been named Pietism." Such thoughts, put forth by individual members in various parts of the German Empire, influenced the spread of dissatisfaction and anti-orthodox resentment spread to the laity until finally "enthusiastic sects and secret societies made their appearance." In its striving for a unified and integrated Christian humanism 'pietism' (Arnold) is clearly distinguished from Luther's piety, which insisted on the actuality and the full preservation of the abysmal dualism between God and the world . . . The ideal goal of the religious cravings of the Pietists was the rebirth of the human soul in Christ . . . . Ancient and seemingly forgotten doctrines revived the movement . . . The beginnings of German immigration in the United States of America are closely linked with the pietistic movement . . . Many leaders of German thought and culture in the following two centuries grew up in the shadow and shelter of this pietistic heritage, acknowledging their debt to a form of spirituality that illumines with its kindly light the years of their intellectual and moral formation," of whom the foremost was Goethe.

141. See Schalk, Adolph, *The Germans*, Prentice-Hall, 1971, p. 436, for the question on "Dutch" versus "Deutsch."

142. Rural Free Delivery was begun in 1886.

143. Wisconsin alone had four regiments made up overwhelmingly of German immigrants. Zeitlin, Richard, "Wisconsin German Populations and the Civil War," speech sponsored by the Max Kade Institute for German-American Studies, May 8, 2003. Dr. Zeitlin is director of the Wisconsin Veterans Museum and adjunct professor of military history at the University of Wisconsin in Madison.

144. *Two Hundred Years*, p. 48-50. "They [the 48ers] had nothing in common with the large groups of immigrant families . . . the typical Forty-Eighter was in his early twenties; he was a freethinker and a member of the 'Burschenschaft' [a student organization with nationalistic, i.e., nation-unifying, aims]; he had risked his

life for freedom, and had now arrived in America without family or belongings. He had often barely managed to avoid arrest, and sometimes he had escaped from prison..."

145. *Two Hundred Years*, p. 48-50. "Carl Schurz . . . the towering figure among the Forty-Eighters . . . joined the [US] Republican Party, supported the presidential campaign of Abraham Lincoln, and in 1861 became Lincoln's first ambassador to Spain. At his own request, he was relieved of this post in Madrid, so that he might serve as a division commander for the Union in the Civil War. As Secretary of Interior . . . under Hayes . . . he pushed through civil service reform, and made the first moves towards integrating the Indians into American Society . . . Schurz' distinctions, however, were not typical of the Forty-Eighters, who were labeled 'Latin Farmers,' that is, academically trained persons who had no notion of farming methods. However, as a whole the Forty-Eighter immigrants worked consistently and loyally toward the ideals in a country other than their homeland."

146. *wsww.doj.state.wi.us/* His wife Margarethe Meyer Schurz founded the first Kindergarten in America in the year 1856 in Watertown, Wisconsin. She started by teaching relatives and neighbors with arts and crafts, music and play, a system which was quickly adopted throughout the United States.

147. Eden Valley is located some 75 miles northwest of Minneapolis.

148. In English a German 'ö' is spelled oe, (as well as the 'ü' which becomes ue), therefore Möhrle becomes Moehrle. Basically an umlauted 'o', is an 'e' spoken with rounded lips, an umlauted 'u', an 'i' with rounded lips, not impossible to sound when put that way. The already alluded to spelling reform in Germany may also do away with the "*Umlaut,*" 'ö' and 'ü.'

149. Refer to the graph on Note # 14.

150. Prohibition was in effect in America from 1920-1933.

Bibliography to Cross Currents: In the Wake of the Great War

Written

Deutschland: Forum für Politik, Kultur, Wirtschaft, und Wissenschaft, Frankfurter Societäts-Drückerei GmbH, D-60268 Frankfurt am Main; website: www.fsd.de

Encyclopedia Britannica 1881.

Eidt, Robert C., Pioneer Settlement in Northeast Argentina, University of Wisconsin Press, Milwaukee, 1971.

Frenzel, H.A. und E., Daten deutscher Dichtung Chronologischer Abriß der deutsche Literatur geschichte, Band I und Band II, Deutscher Taschenbuch Verlag GmbH & Co., München.

German Life, Zeitgeist Publishing, Grantsville, MD.

Germany, Fodor's 2000.

Germany, Insight Guides, 1998.

Grant, Sue, German Life, "100 Years-Steiff Teddy Bears," December 2002/July 2003, pp.38-39.

Goethe, Johann Wolfgang von, Deutsche Gedichte, Echtermeyer, revision Benno von Wiese, August Basel Verlag, Duisberg, 1956.

Hesse, Karen, Letters from Rifka, Puffin Books, 1992.

Kramer, Dieter, German Holidays and Folk Customs, Atlantik Brücke, 1973.

Levine, Ellen, If Your Name Was Changed at Ellis Island, Scholastic, N.Y., 1993.

Mann, Heinrich, Der Untertan, (The Underling),1918.

Reeves, Pamela, Ellis Island: Gateway to the American Dream, Barnes & Noble, N.Y., 1998.

Reinhardt, Kurt F., Germany: 2000 Years, v. I, "The Rise and Fall of the Holy Roman Empire," Frederick Ungar Publishing, N.Y., 1969.

Reinhardt, Kurt F., Germany: 2000 Years, v. II, "The Second Empire and the Weimar Republic," Frederick Ungar, N.Y., 1971.

Schalk, Adolph, *The Germans*, Prentice-Hall, 1971.

Selig, Robert, *German Life*, "Germans in Russia," Dc 2000/Jy, 2001, pp. 42-44.

Twain, Mark, "A Tramp Abroad," *A Connecticut Yankee in King Arthur's Court*.

Two Hundred Years of German-American Relations 1776-1976: A Documentary, Thomas Piltz, ed., Heinz Moos Verlag, München, (a bilingual book in English and German), 1975.

Waterman, John T., *A History of the German Language*, University of Washington Press, Seattle, 1976.

Internet

http://csmweb2.emcweb.com/durable/1999/

http://www.csmonitor.com/durable/1999/10/01/fp8s2-csm.shtml

http://www.nobel.se/literature/laureates/1972/press.html (Heinrich Böll)

http://www.germantv.dw-world.de

http://wsww.doj.state.wi.us/

http://www.capanamur.org/afghanistan

http://www.centre.telemanage.ca/quotes.nsf

http://www.germantv.de

http://www.goethe.de/fr/nan/deelysee.htm

http://www.mwsc.edu/orgs/germanclub/inflation2.html

http://www.suntimes.com/output/ebert1/wkp-news-nowhere21f.html

http://www.wisc.edu/mki

Lectures

Zeitlin, Richard, "Wisconsin German Populations and the Civil War," sponsored by the Max Kade Institute for German-American Studies, University of Wisconsin in Madison, May 8, 2003.

About the Author

The daughter of a German immigrant father and a German-American mother, Marita Ritsche developed a lifelong interest in social history and a special interest in German immigration to the Americas. In addition to a master's degree in German, Marita has completed forty-five credits, mostly in foreign universities, such as, in Salzburg, Madrid, Guatemala, and Guadalajara. She lived three years in Germany, during one of which she taught English in a high school in Wolfsburg. In 1987 she accompanied her father, siblings, sons and her uncle's family for a transatlantic family reunion of some sixty persons in Meersburg, her father's birthplace. Impressions of this journey, until now latent, came to fruition in this book. In addition to her love of writing and of world languages, Marita is dedicated to ecological and social justice concerns. She lives in Milwaukee, Wisconsin, with her ever inquisitive *Kätzchen*, whom she swears purrs with an accent.

Cross Currents

By Marita Ritsche

To order copies of *Cross Currents*, please complete the form below. (Feel free to duplicate this form.)

I would like to order_____ copies of *Cross Currents* at $17.00 per copy (plus postage and handling.)

Book Total
(_____ copies at $17.00) $_____

Sales Tax
(Wisconsin residents add 5.6%) $_____
Shipping and Handling

($4.00 for first book; $2.00 for each additional) $_____

Total Amount Enclosed $_____
Checks should be made payable to: *Transfluency Press.*
Please do not send cash.

Ordered by:

Name _____
Address _____
City _____
State _____ Zip _____
Phone Number (_____)_____

Ship to: **(if different from above):**

Name _____
Address _____
City _____
State _____ Zip _____
Phone Number (_____)_____

Please complete this order form and mail to:
Transfluency Press, 1527 W. County Line Rd., Milwaukee, WI 53217